THE CHARLTON STANDARD CATALOGUE OF CANADIAN GOVERNMENT PAPER MONEY

THIRD EDITION

W.K. CROSS
Publisher

The Charlton Press
15 BIRCH AVE.
TORONTO, CANADA
M4V 1E1

I

ACKNOWLEDGEMENTS

The Charlton Press wish to thank all those who have helped and assisted in the third edition of the Charlton Standard Catalogue of Canadian Government Paper Money.

Editorial

Editor	– Walter D. Allan
Associate Editor	– Robert J. Graham
Assistant Editor	– M. P. Cross
Layout	– Frank Van Lieshout
Cover Note	– Walter D. Allan Collection

Current Contributors

Paul Berry   Al Bliman   Harry Eisenhauer
Graham Esler   Michael Findlay   Ronald A. Greene
Lub Wojtiw

Past Contributors

G.H. Bishop   Sheldon S. Carroll   J.A. Haxby
E.R. Hunter   W.E. Ireland   R.D. Lockwood
A.B. McCullough   Ruth McQuade*   J.A. Peddie*
R. Stewart Taylor

Institutions

Bank of Canada, National Currency Collection   Canadian Bankers Association
Canadian Imperial Bank of Commerce   Bank of Montreal
Bank of Nova Scotia   Royal Bank of Canada
Toronto Dominion Bank

A great deal of credit must go to Robert J. Graham who, without preparation of the original manuscript, the third, of course, would be impossible.

Corrections

The publishers welcome information, for future editions, from interested collectors and dealers concerning any aspect of the listings in this book.

CONTENTS

INTRODUCTION

The Transition to an Irredeemable Government Paper Currency

For over a hundred years banks and governments engaged in a struggle for the lucrative right to issue paper currency. The banks at first succeeded in keeping the various governments pretty well shut out. This was fortunate because notes of the reputable chartered banks represented cash while government issues often represented the lack of it. Bank notes were generally redeemable in gold or silver, while governments often backed their notes only by securities based on land, of which there was an almost inexhaustible supply, or by the promise of anticipated revenues. The Province of Canada succeeded in making a major intrusion into the banks' prerogative in 1866, and thereafter the government continuously nibbled note-issuing privileges away until 1945, when it became illegal for banks to issue any more of their notes for circulation in Canada.

In the early colonial days, before Confederation, the issue of paper currency was almost exclusively a function of the chartered banks. The right to issue bank notes was a very valuable one, effectively providing the bank with an interest-free loan from the time it issued one of its notes until it redeemed it in specie (gold or silver coin). The usual lending rate was around six per cent per annum and the circulation of notes provided banks with one of their principal sources of revenue.

Provincial and municipal governments were fully aware of the benefits of a paper currency to its issuer, and sometimes plotted jealously to obtain some of those benefits for themselves. The municipal councils of urban centres including Toronto, Kingston, Hamilton, London and others issued notes over the period from the late 1830's to the early 1860's. The provincial governments of New Brunswick, Nova Scotia, Prince Edward Island and Newfoundland issued Treasury Notes. The Treasury Notes of Prince Edward Island and Nova Scotia were often poorly secured and difficult to redeem, causing them to circulate at a discount to the detriment of their reputation. In the Canadas, New Brunswick and Newfoundland, these municipal and provincial forms of paper money usually did not constitute a very substantial part of the currency, and for the most part offered the banks little serious competition.

The Province of Canada, formed in 1841 by the union of Upper and Lower Canada, was in dire need of financing with distressing regularity, sometimes for public works and sometimes just to pay the interest on previous loans. The government was so deeply in debt that its credit with the banks and European lending houses had reached its limit. In 1841 the Governor General, Lord Sydenham, proposed a government-issued paper currency, redeemable on demand, to pay for an ambitious public works programme. The banks, which stood to lose their note-issuing privileges under the plan. resisted and Sydenham's proposal was defeated. As a consolation measure, the banks were taxed one per cent of their circulation, and thus had to turn over to the government a small share of the proceeds arising from their note issues.

Various municipal and other governments then met their need for financing by issuing interest-bearing debentures, which looked like bank notes and could and to an extent did circulate as money. Denominations varied from a $1 note issued by the District of Wellington to a $100 note issued by the United Counties of Leeds and Grenville. The Province of Canada briefly issued $1, $2, $10 and $20 debentures.

Financial woes prompted the Province of Canada Government to make another attempt in 1860 to replace bank notes over a period of time by government notes. Again the banks prevailed, and A. T. Galt, the Inspector-General, was forced to abandon his plan. In 1866 the Provincial Government was again embarrassed, its funds being locked up in the tottering Bank of Upper Canada. In league with its new banker, the Bank of Montreal, the government issued Province of Canada notes in denominations from $1 to $1000. Our present currency system has its origin in these Provincial notes.

Abetted by the Bank of Montreal, the first Dominion Government sought to introduce a system comparable to the new American model, the National Banking System. Under this scheme a uniform currency backed by government securities would be issued by the banks. The other banks as usual were opposed, since they would be forced into buying securities which would pay interest only for the first ten years, and because the circulation would lose its flexibility which was needed to allow for seasonal expansion for "moving the crops". Again the banks were able to muster enough support to defeat the proposal.

The new Finance Minister, Sir Francis Hincks, had the wisdom to realize that a piecemeal approach would be more successful. His legislation of 1870 and 1871 generally removed from the banks the right to issue $1 and $2 notes, which would be issued by the Dominion Government, (some of the eastern banks, as well as one or two others, were exempted for special reasons). The notes of $4 and up were left to the banks. Some banks then took such heroic measures as the issue of $6 and $7 notes to avoid the use of Dominion notes wherever possible and thus maximize their own circulations. The loophole was plugged in 1881 when the Dominion Government assumed the right to issue $4 notes, a denomination which was considered useful then because it corresponded to One Pound in the old Halifax currency, while restricting most banks to issues of $5 and its multiples. The banks were also required to hold a greater part of their reserves in Dominion notes. The high denomination Dominion notes were principally used for this purpose.

The Bank Act of 1890 provided some fine tuning for a system which had worked tolerably well for the previous two decades. Bank notes were made redeemable at par at all branches of the issuing institution throughout the country, and a redemption fund was established to guarantee the notes of any bank which might subsequently fail. Thereafter no note of a Canadian bank depreciated as the result of the failure of the issuing bank. In 1912 $5 Dominion notes entered circulation, in competition with chartered bank issues.

With the outbreak of World War I in 1914, drastic changes were made in anticipation of currency upheavals resulting from the war. The gold standard was suspended, bank notes were declared legal tender, and the redemption of Dominion notes was suspended. Paper money became in effect irredeemable, but little panic ensued apart from a few minor runs on banks. The gold standard was partially restored from 1926 to 1929, when the Depression brought on a growing awareness of the need for a central bank and a centrally managed economy.

When the Bank of Canada began business in 1935, the banks were given ten years to reduce their note circulation to 25 per cent of their paid-up capital. Bank of Canada notes would make up an increasing proportion of the currency and replace the Dominion notes, which were rapidly being withdrawn. The 1944 revision of the Bank Act removed the right of the banks to issue or reissue any of their notes at all after the end of that year except outside Canada, where the circulation was limited to 10 per cent of the capital. In 1950 the banks paid over to the Bank of Canada a sum corresponding to their outstanding notes, and in 1954 even the right to issue notes outside of Canada was removed. The long process of establishing an irredeemable currency issued solely by the government was complete.

The Charlton Catalogue Numbering System

The numbering system used for several years to identify notes issued by the Province of Canada, the Dominion of Canada and the Bank of Canada has been modified in this catalogue to accomodate newly discovered varieties. The renumbering should not be too great an inconvenience for collectors, and since the listing of all notes except for current issues is now believed to be complete, no further changes should be necessary in future editions.

Each identifying number begins with a letter code indicating the issuing authority, as follows:

A	–Alberta	NB	–New Brunswick
BC	–Bank of Canada	NF	–Newfoundland
BrC	–British Columbia	NS	–Nova Scotia
DC	–Dominion of Canada	PEI	–Prince Edward Island
PC	–Province of Canada	UC	–Provisional Government
			of Upper Canada

The number that follows refers to the type (basic design) of the note. If varieties of major significance occur within the basic type, such as changes in signatures, seals, colour of back, domicile or border pattern, these are indicated by lower case letters following the number. Minor varieties such as change in the imprint or hyphenation of a series letter are distinguished by lower case Roman numerals.

Numbers Printed, Scarcity and Prices

It seems obvious that notes which were printed in small quantities should be scarce and accordingly command substantial prices. There are, however, several factors which may disturb this simple relationship. First, notes most recently printed often have a higher survival rate. For instance, the "no letter" 1870 "shinplasters" were printed in the smallest quantities of the three varieties. Yet they are the commonest because they were the latest to be issued, after most of the A series and many of the B series were worn out and destroyed. Secondly, notes which have turned up in hoards tend to be more readily available, distorting the relationship between number issued and scarcity. As an example, more 1912- $5 "Train" notes were printed in the series A than in the series B "seal over" type. The former are nevertheless scarcer because no hoards have been found. A corollary to this fact is lower denomination notes tended to be held as mementoes while high denominations represented more money than many individuals were able to set aside. Finally, price is determined not only by the survival rate and consequent scarcity of a note, but also by the collector demand for it. This is determined by the appeal and popularity of a note or series. The 1935 Bank of Canada $25 note does not rank among the rare Canada notes, but its high price attests to its popularity.

Where a large number of series occurs within a given issue and variety of Dominion notes these have been recorded in detail as far as possible in this catalogue, but they have not been individually priced. The same applies to the Bank of Canada regular issues and asterisk notes. Although numerous series or prefixes may be priced together, it is certain that they are not all equally available. If the trend to collect by series or prefix continues to develop, these may be priced separately in later editions.

Subsidiary Information

Designs and Colours: The main vignettes appearing on each note are described in the same order as they occur on the notes, with oblique lines separating description, e.g., beaver/ship/cattle. Where there is no vignette illustrating a particular portion of the note, a dash (-) appears in place of the description.

Imprint: The banknote company imprint is given for each note or issue. The imprint indicates the company that engraved the plates and/or printed the notes from them. The dual imprint, e.g., "ABNCo. and BABN" indicates plates originally engraved by the American Bank Note Company that were later used by the British American Bank Note Company for printing notes.

Signature Details: For each issue, all of the printed and some of the manuscript (mss.) (handwritten with pen and ink) signatures are given. There are two kinds of printed signatures, engraved (engr.) and typographed (typed).

Engraved signatures are engraved into the face plate and are printed at the same time as the face design. For notes printed from the same part of a plate, the positions of the engraved signatures relative to the frame do not vary.

Typed signatures, however, are added as overprints after the rest of the note has been printed. Consequently, the signatues may be found to be in slightly different positions when the notes are compared. Typed signatures also usually have flat, broad strokes in contrast to the thin, raised strokes of the engraved signatures.

Dating: Where the notes are fully dated by mechanical means, whether by engraving or letterpress (typography), the dates are listed in the form:

Engraved	Letterpress
Jan. 2, 1845	Jan. 2, 1845

This form is used regardless of whether the day of the month occurs before or after the month on the actual notes.

Partially engraved dates are listed with blanks where some information was left to be filled in manuscript, and the completed dates, if known, follow in the form:

Partially Engraved 18__

Jan. 2, 1845

Overprints and Stamps: Overprints, extra details added by a printing press after the notes have otherwise been completed, are listed for each issue. Stamps differ from overprints in being added by hand, with a rubber or wooded implement. If an overprint appears on separate lines on the note, this is indicated by an oblique (/), e.g., PROVINCIAL NOTE/LEGAL TENDER/PAYABLE IN MONTREAL/FOR THE RECEIVER GENERAL.

Remainders, Proofs and Specimens: Whenever possible, fully completed notes (those signed, numbered and dated) are listed. In cases where fully completed notes are not known or when other forms are much more common, remainders, proofs or specimens are listed.

A remainder is a regular note which has not had all of the blanks filled in. Remainders are sometimes encountered with spurious signatures, dates, etc.; this does not change their status. Failing the availability of completed remainder notes either specimens or proofs are listed.

A specimen is not intended for circulation, but is used to acquaint bank employees and others with the characteristics of the genuine notes. It is usually printed on banknote paper with face and back designs same as issued issuable notes; however, it usually has serial numbers consisting of all 0's and is overprinted or stamped "SPECIMEN" usually in the signature or sheet number areas.

Proofs are trial or sample impressions taken from the printing plates on very thin paper backed with card and some are printed directly on card. They often have no serial numbers and may or may not be stamped with the word "SPECIMEN". Proofs can be distinguished from specimens insofar as proofs are usually printed only on one side and are not printed on banknote paper. Where it is known that Proofs were made only from the face of the note, "FACE PROOF" is indicated.

Grading

When grading a note it is essential to first determine if the note may be safely removed from its holder without causing any damage due to brittleness, unseen tears, glue remnants, etc. Then, carefully remove the note and holding it lightly, consider the general appearance, amount of wear, the hue and intensity of the colour of both the face and back. Determine a preliminary grade. If the note is Fine or bet6ter it should be held obliquely in line with a good light source. Move it around at various angles, such that the light will reflect off the note highlighting any ripples, counting creases, heavy creases, pressed out creases, tears, pinholes, cancellations, repairs or fading. The mastering of this technique is mandatory in successfully grading paper money. Then these have been carefully considered, one must decide if these are "normal" for the preliminary grade which was determined. If not, then the grade may have to be reduced depending on the number and severity of the defects, or the defects will have to be listed in addition to the overall grade, followed by any unusual defect, than to down grade the note.

Careful inspection to determine the correct grade will lead to greater trust and confidence between buyers and sellers of notes.

UNCIRCULATED UNC. – A perfect note. Crisp and clean as when printed and without any creases or pinholes. Colours have original hue and intensity.

ABOUT UNCIRCULATED AU – Similar to Uncirculated, but it will have either a very light fold or ripple "counting creases," to the extent that the paper fibers are not broken. If any combination of the two are present, the note would fall into the extremely fine grade.

It has been common practice, by some, to add a "plus", "+", "about" or "almost" to infer a slightly higher or lower condition than the designated grade. Eg. about VF, VF +, almost EF.

EXTREMELY FINE EF – Very crisp, clean and colourful as an uncirculated note, but has a major crease or several minor creases. The note may or may not show some slight evidence of wear.

VERY FINE VF – A fairly crisp and clean note. It may have several major and minor crease and folds, some evidence of wear especially along the edges or at the corners. There may be some slight decrease in hue and intensity of the colours. The design in the creases should not be worn off.

FINE F – A note with considerable evidence of circulation. Numerous creases and folds, but a small degree of firmness remaining. Usually fairly soiled and the hue and intensity of the colour are slightly reduced. There may be a slight amount of the design worn off along the major creases.

VERY GOOD VG – A heavily circulated note but with all the major design still visible. Usually limp with no crispness or firmness, quite soiled, hue and intensity of the colour will be faded or altered. A moderate amount of the design may be worn off along the major creases or in the "counting crease" areas. Numerous other defects may apply (see list below).

GOOD G – Similar to VG, but often with tears and small pieces missing. Usually some of the major design is worn off. Signatures and sheet numbers are often unreadable. The note is very limp and usually has numerous other defects.

FAIR F – Similar to Good, but larger pieces missing. Signatures and sheet numbers entirely missing. Often has numerous tears and other defects.

POOR P – As a Fair note, but with a major portion of the note torn off or the design obliterated. Often numerous tape repairs. Generally collectable only because of rarity.

In addition, to accurately grade a note it is necessary to consider any additional impairments. These should include:

1. Minor counting creases or edge defects, especially for UNC and EF grades.
2. Tears, pinholes or signature perforations.
3. Stains, smudges, crayon marks or writing.
4. Missing corners, cut and punch cancellations or edge defects.
5. Undesirable rubber stamps.
6. Any repairs, such as with sticky tape, scotch tape, stamp hinges, etc.
7. Chemical damage, paste or glue from attachment to a page.
8. Poorly centered or badly trimmed edges.

Proof, specimen and essay notes are commonly accepted as being in uncirculated condition, otherwise, they should be described as impaired with the type and degree of impairment stated.

Useful Terminology and Information

KINDS OF FRAUDULENT NOTES

Counterfeit: A facsimile copy of a note of a legitimate bank.
Raised: A note which has been fraudulently modified so as to appear to be of higher denomination.

PARTS OF NOTES

Face: The front of a note, sometimes incorrectly referred to as the obverse.
Back: The subordinate side of a note sometimes incorrectly called the reverse. Many notes were printed with blank or "plain" backs.
Vignette: An engraved picture (portrait or scene) on a bank note.
Counter: A word, letter or number indicating the denomination of a note.
Payee: The person or organization to whom a note is made payable. The payee on many modern notes is simply referred to as "the bearer".
Domicile: The specific branch or branches where the note was made payable.
Tint: The background coloured design found on notes. The tint is printed before the face or back plate, as opposed to a protector, which is an overprint. In the 19th century tints were usually printed by the engraved plate method. Gradually, beginning in the late 19th century, banknote companies switched over to printing tints by lithography.

Plate Number: In many cases, notes can be traced to the plates used in printing them by means of plate numbers. These are tiny numbers inobtrusively printed on the notes, each having a face plate number on one side and a back plate number on the other. Where plate numbers are not present on the notes, these were often printed on the salvage, or waste paper on the edges of the sheet of notes and trimmed off before the notes were issued.

PRINTING METHODS

Letterpress:
(Typography)
In this process the design is the highest part of the printing plate and is flat. When the plate is inked only the design receives the ink by virtue of its location. Letterpress results in a fairly thick and flat layer of ink on the note. Sheet numbers, protectors and most overprints were added by this method of printing.

Engraved Plate:
(Intaglio)
The design is cut into a flat sheet of metal, and in contrast to letterpress the design is below the flat upper surface of the plate. The plate is inked and the flat surface wiped clean, leaving ink only in the recessed (engraved) areas which is transferred to the paper during printing. The resulting image has a 3-dimensional character. Most parts of the notes were printed by this means since it made possible the highest resolution of fine lines and the most life-like portraits. This method also provided the best security against the practice of counterfeiting.

Lithography:
In the latter part of the 19th century lithography was used to print the coloured background (tint) on some notes. As it was practiced then, lithography involved the photography of a design and its transfer via a negative to the surface of a special stone coated with a layer of a photosensitive material. After treatment, only the image on the stone would pick up ink. This type of printing resulted in the transfer of a thin flat layer of ink.

THE NUMBERING OF DOMINION NOTES

Sheet Number:
Province of Canada and Dominion of Canada notes were usually numbered in sheets of four, each note having the same number. This is called the sheet number. Many people mistakenly refer to the sheet number as the "serial number".

Check Letter:
Since more than one note in a sheet could bear the same number, each note was provided with a distinguishing letter, a **check letter**. Check letter A, B, C and D were used for sheets of four notes. In later years Dominion notes were printed on larger sheets, up to 24/on (i.e., sheets of 24 notes). However, these were still numbered in groups of four notes, with check letters A, B, C and D. The 25-cent fractional notes of 1923 were numbered in sheets of ten, all having the same sheet number, so check letters A, B, C, D, E, H, J, K, L and M were used.

Series Letter:
For a particularly large issue of notes, where the available sheet numbers had all been used, the same numbers would be started over again, accompanied by a new **series letter**. A different series letter would be used for each successive cycle of sheet numbers. The first usage of a series letter on Dominion notes occurs on the 1878 $1 issue, where the first series was "plain" (i.e., no letter), followed in turn by series A, B, and C. The use of a "plain" series to initiate a new issue was discontinued by the end of the nineteenth century, and thereafter new issues began with series A. Before the 1923 Dominion note issue, series letters were variously printed preceding or following the sheet number or in other locations on the note face. The precise locations are explained in the text for each issue where necessary. From 1923 to 1935 the series letter always preceded the sheet number.

Serial Number:
From the above it should be clear that the serial number, the designation that uniquely identifies a note, must include not only the sheet number but

also the check letter and the series letter if they are present. The check letter is normally written last, separated from the rest of the serial number by an oblique line. Thus the serial number C6364208/D denotes sheet number 6364208, check letter D, in series C.

THE NUMBERING OF BANK OF CANADA NOTES

The 1935 issue of Bank of Canada notes used the same numbering system as the Dominion notes. For later issues the system was substantially changed. Since 1937 check letters have not been used. Complete specification of the serial number requires two (or, very recently, three) prefix letters and the number on the note. For the $5 and $20 notes of the 1979 issue, the serial number consists only of an eleven-digit number.

The Distribution Network for Canadian Government Notes

The Province of Canada notes were issued by the branches of the Bank of Montreal, the only chartered bank willing to surrender the privilege of issuing its own notes. This arrangement continued for a few years after Confederation. During that period 170-72 branches of the Receiver General's Department called A.R.G. (Assistant Receiver General) offices were established in the largest city in each province and gradually assumed the functions of issue and redemption. In this transitional period some shipments of Dominion notes were made directly from the Receiver General's Department to the chartered banks. Additional A.R.G. offices were established as new provinces were added to the Dominion.

When the Bank of Canada took over the government note issue, branches of the bank were established in each province. These branches took care of the distribution of Bank of Canada notes to financial institutions within their respective provinces. Banks and individuals have also been able to acquire notes directly from the Bank of Canada in Ottawa.

FRATERNAL ORGANIZATIONS

Listed below are a number of organizations dedicated to the preservation, study and enjoyment of paper currency. All will be delighted to hear from collectors interested in any aspect of paper money collecting.

The Canadian Paper Money Society

Established in 1964 and incorporated in 1972, the Society is a non-profit, historical and educational organization interested in Canadian bank notes, banking, and other Canadian paper money. It publishes *The Canadian Paper Money Journal* quarterly and has library and other facilities available. The Society is sustained by regular members' contributions of $20.00 per year or $300.00 Life Membership donation to the Income Trust Fund. The official address of the Society is P.O. Box 465, West Hill Post Office, West Hill, Ontario, Canada, M1E 2P0.

The Canadian Numismatic Association

The CNA was founded in 1950 and incorporated in 1963. It is a non-profit educational association which has members in every province in Canada, every state in the U.S. and many other countries. Its objective is to encourage and promote the science of numismatics by acquirement and study of coins, paper money, medals, tokens, and all other numismatic items with special emphasis on material pertaining to Canada. Membership includes use of the associations library material as well as a subscription to *The Canadian Numismatic Journal*, a monthly magazine devoted to Canadian numismatics. Annual membership fees are $25.00 for those over 21 years of age, $12.50 for those under the age of 21, $35.00 for a family membership and $25.00 for a club, society, library or other non-profit organization. Life memberships, $400. The current executive secretary is Mr. Kenneth B. Prophet and he may be reached at P.O. Box 226, Barrie, Ontario, Canada, L4M 4T2.

The Canadian Prefix Newsletter

The Canadian Prefix Newsletter (CPN) is a non-profit publication which began in July of 1975 and is devoted to providing information about Canadian prefixes and related printed matter. Its aims are to assist collectors in becoming more informed about the hobby and to further their enjoyment of paper money. The CPN is published four times a year (January, April, July and October) and annual subscriptions consist of a minimum $6.00 donation payable to the secretary-treasurer. The current editor is Dr. L. Wojtiw and he may be reached at 3548 104th Street, Edmonton, Albert, Canada, T6J 2J7.

The International Bank Note Society

The IBNS was founded in 1961 and now has a membership of over 1,500 with representation from over 60 countries. The current annual dues (in U.S. funds) are as follows:
Regular Membership $17.50, Family Membership $22.50 and Junior Membership $9.00. Life Memberships are also available for $300.00 U.S. The Society publishes the *IBNS Journal* quarterly which is distributed free of charge (by surface mail) to its members. The current general secretary is Mr. Milan Alusic, P.O. Box 1222, Racine, Wisonsin, 53405, U.S.A.

Society of Paper Money Collectors

In June 1964 the Society was incorporated as a non-profit organization under the laws of the District of Columbia. Membership now numbers approximately 2,300 the majority of which reside in Canada and the U.S. but there is representation throughout the world. The SPMC publishes *Paper Money* bimonthly in the odd months and sends it to its members. Dues are $12.00 (U.S.) per year. Those interested should contact Mr. Ronald Horstman, New Member Co-ordination, P.O. Box 6011, St. Louis, Missouri, 63139, U.S.A.

The Essay-Proof Society

This Society was organized in 1943 and meets at the Collectors Club in New York City at 8 o'clock in the evening on the second Wednesday of each month (except January, July and August). It publishes *The Essay-Proof Journal* which is available for $20.00 (U.S.) per year. Current membership dues are $20.00 (U.S.) per year. Further information may be obtained from Mr. David E. McGuire, Secretary, RD #4, Colonial Drive, Katonah, New York, 10536, U.S.A.

FRENCH COLONIAL ISSUES

Playing Card Money
1685-1719

Desperate for funds to pay the troops stationed in New France, the Intendant wrote pledges on the backs of playing cards in June 1685. Because of the illiteracy of the inhabitants, the cards were cut in halves or quarters to assist in the recognition of denominations — four livres on a whole card, two livres on half a card and fifteen sols on a quarter card. When specie arrived from France in September, the playing cards were all redeemed.

Despite the King's disapproval of the practice of issuing card money, the failure of the supply ships to arrive on time (or at all) forced the colonial administration to resort to its issue again and again. At first the system worked well, the playing cards being promptly redeemed. After 1700 the French Treasury was often unable to pay the amounts appropriated for New France and the shortfall had to be made up by more playing card money, with no immediate prospect of redemption. Inflation was the predictable result. In 1714 the King of France offered to redeem the playing card money at fifty per cent of its face value, in silver. By 1720 virtually all of the playing cards had been redeemed and burned, and any not turned in for redemption were proclaimed worthless. Over the next ten years no card money circulated in New France. Coin was scarce because it was hoarded by the habitants rather than lent out at interest, "usury" being offensive to their religious beliefs. The colony was once again plagued by the lack of a circulating currency.

50 Livres, 1714

Card Money
1729-1757
QUEBEC CITY

New card money appeared again in 1729, on plain white cardboard. This and later issues were sanctioned by the King. The card money was redeemable in bills of exchange which were in turn to be redeemed regularly in silver coin. The cards were clipped in various ways to indicate the denomination. They were signed (or, in the case of smaller cards, initiallied) by the Governor and the Intendant, who also affixed their seals to the notes. Again the system worked well at first, the cards being preferred by the habitants even to the bills of exchange on France by which they were to be redeemed. They then began to hoard the cards, which necessitated that more and more be issued, with inadequate means of redemption. After the fall of New France, the card money was redeemed at one-quarter of its face value.

12 livres, 1749

6 Livres, 1735

24 Livres, 1735

Denom.	Issue Date	G	VG	F	VF
7 sols 6 deniers	1749				
15 sols	1749, 1757				
20 sols	1734				
30 sols	1733, 1738, 1752, 1757	ALL CARD MONEY IS VERY RARE			
3 livres	1742, 1747, 1749	Estimate: G-$1,000. to VF-$2,500.			
6 livres	1729, 1735, 1749				
12 livres	1729, 1730, 1733, 1735, 1742, 1747, 1749				
24 livres	1729, 1730, 1733, 1735, 1742, 1749				

2

Ordonnances or Treasury Notes
QUEBEC CITY

Orders on the local treasury, or treasury notes, began to circulate in the 1730's in increasing quantity, overshadowing the amount of card money in circulation. These notes were issued to pay for military expenditures. The amount of treasury notes expanded rapidly after 1743, while the more reputable card money was hoarded. During the last years of the French Regime, treasury notes were issued in extravagant amounts to meet the cost of war with England, despite the exhausted state of the treasury. By 1759 they totalled thirty million livres. An even greater sum in bills of exchange on France were in circulation. The amount of paper in circulation in 1760 was fifteen times greater than in 1750, and once again severe inflation was the result. With the cession of New France to England, the status of all the treasury notes and bills of exchange was rendered even more dubious.

Sharp English merchants trading in Canada bought up the discredited paper at one-sixth of face value or even less. After the Treaty of Paris and subsequent negotiations, bills of exchange were redeemed in specie at half of their face value (although some were paid in full). Treasury notes were paid at one-quarter of face value, with some additional indemnification for holders who were British subjects. The harsh experiences of the habitants with a poorly secured paper circulation resulted in a deep mistrust of paper money which endured for generations.

48 livres, 1753

96 Livres, 1757

Denom.	Issue Date	G	VG	F	VF
20 sols	1754, 1757, 1758, 1759				
3 livres	1756, 1758				
6 livres	1758, 1759				
12 livres	1757, 1758, 1759		ALL TREASURY NOTES ARE RARE		
24 livres	1753, 1756		Estimate: G-$1,000. to VF-$2,500.		
48 livres	1753, 1758				
96 livres	1757, 1759				

ARMY BILLS
Issues of 1813-1815

Army bills were issued for the purchase of supplies and the payment of troops during the War of 1812 to 1814. Normally these military expenditures were met by the sale of bills of exchange drawn on the British Treasury. However when war broke out the greatly increased sums required could only be raised from the small amount of specie in the country, if at all, by heavily discounting the bills of exchange. To meet this situation, legal tender notes were issued from the Army Bill Office in Quebec City which had been established for that purpose.

I. FIRST ISSUE, 1813

The army bills were first issued in 1813 in denominations of $4, $25, $50, $100 and $400. The denominations of $25 and up were made to bear interest at the rate of 1d per L100 currency ($400) per day, or 6 1/12% per annum. They were redeemable in cash or bills of exchange on London, at the option of the Commander of the Forces. These notes, which were in reality investment securities, were not reissuable after redemption. The $4 notes on the other hand were reissuable and did not bear interest. They were redeemable in specie on demand. Notes of this issue are quite large, measuring about 5 1/4" x 7 1/2".

Two manuscript signatures were applied when the notes were issued, over the headings, CASHIER and DIRECTOR. Denominations were given in Spanish-American dollars only. Each note was printed with a wide variety of sizes and styles of type as a security measure. In addition, each note was printed with a counterfoil at the left, consisting of the spelled-out denomination in alternating English and French, in graduated sizes of type. The counterfoil was bisected when the note was issued, and if the stub portion did not match the note portion upon presentation for redemption, any attempted counterfeiting would be exposed.

$4

Face Design: Crest of Prince of Wales   **Back Design:** Plain
Colour: Black

Issue Date: Partially Engraved   **Imprint:** None
May 1813 or June 1813
Signatures
Left: mss. various   **Right:** mss. various

Denom.	Issue Date	G	VG	F	VF	EF	Unc
$4	1813	VERY RARE–Estimate: $1,500. to $4,000.					

PHOTO NOT AVAILABLE

$25-$400

Face Design: Royal Crest/—/—
Colour: Black

Back Design: Plain
Imprint: None

Issue Date: Partially Engraved
_____1813
May 1 or June 15 1813
Signatures
Left: mss. various

Right: mss. various

Denom.	Issue Date	G	VG	F	VF	EF	Unc
$25	1813						
$50	1813			ALL VERY RARE			
$100	1813			Estimate: $1,500. to $4,000.			
$400	1813						

II. SECOND ISSUE, CA. 1813

Historical records imply that there was a second issue of army bills, probably dated late in 1813. It consisted of non-interest bearing denominations of $1, $2, $8, $10, $12, $16 and $20. The other details of this issue are unknown, and no notes are known to have survived.

III. THIRD ISSUE, 1814

The third issue of army bills is dated March 1814 and consisted of non-interest bearing denominations of $1, $2, $3, $5 and $10, with the equivalent amounts also stated in shillings (Halifax currency). These have counterfoils at the left consisting of the word "BON" in graduated sizes, with alternating normal and italicized characters. Notes of this issue bear a single signature but are also initialled at the left. They were redeemable in government bills of exchange on London. Notes of this issue are much smaller, measuring about 2 1/2" x 4". Large black capital letters appear in the upper left corners, which relate to the denomination as follows:

G/$1, H/$2, I/$3. K/$5 and L/$10

$1 (5s.)

Face Design: No Vignettes   **Back Design:** Plain
Colour: Black

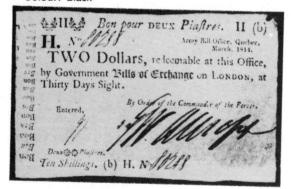

$2 (10s.)

Face Design: No Vignettes   **Back Design:** Plain
Colour: Black

$3 (15s.)

Face Design: No Vignettes   **Back Design:** Plain
Colour: Black

$5 (25s.)

Face Design: No Vignettes   **Back Design:** Plain
Colour: Black

$10 (50s.)

Face Design:	No Vignettes	Back Design:	Plain

Colour: Black

Issue Date:	Engraved	Imprint:	None

March 1814
May 1814
August 1814

Signatures: mss. various

Denom.	Issue Date	G	VG	F	VF	EF	Unc
$1 (5s.)	1814	VERY RARE – Estimate: $1,500. to $4,000.
$2 (10s.)	1814	VERY RARE – Estimate: $1,500. to $4,000.
$3 (15s.)	1814	VERY RARE – Estimate: $1,500. to $4,000.
$5 (25s.)	1814	VERY RARE – Estimate: $1,500. to $4,000.
$10 (50s.)	1814	VERY RARE – Estimate: $1,500. to $4,000.

IV. FINAL QUEBEC ISSUE, 1815

Only $10 notes of the January 1815 issue have been recorded, although other denominations were probably issued. Like the previous issue, a large M at the top seems to be associated with the denomination. The counterfoil at the left consists of the words "dix Piastres" and "Exchange" alternately in various sizes and styles of type. The notes are of the large 5 1/4" x 7 1/2" format.

The authorized extent of all issues totalled $6,000,000, and at the end of the war about $4,996,000 remained outstanding. Of this, about $3,000,000 was in the larger interest-bearing denominations. The notes were rapidly redeemed after the war ended, with the provinces paying the interest and the British Treasury paying the principal.

Their use coincided with a period of wartime prosperity, brought on by high prices for produce coupled with a massive influx of capital from Great Britain. The fact that the notes could always be readily converted into cash went a long way toward ending the deep distrust of paper money by the French Canadian population, who had learned from the harsh lesson of the French Regime paper that it was better to hoard coin. Since the army bills were virtually all redeemed in 1815, after which date no further interest was allowed, they are now very scarce.

$10 (50s.)

Face Design:	Cornucopia, ribbons and leaves/—/tiny crest on bottom	**Back Design:**	Plain
Colour:	Black		
Issue Date:	Engraved January 1815	**Imprint:**	None
		Signatures:	mss. various

Denom.	Issue Date	G	VG	F	VF	EF	Unc
$10 (50s.)	1815	VERY RARE – Estimate: $1,500. to $4,000.					

V. MICHILMACKINAC TYPE

Although only one army bill is known to have been established, the one at Quebec City, a note having the appearance of an army bill issued at Michilmackinac has been discovered. Michilmackinac Island was captured by the British in 1812 and restored to the United States after the war ended. This $4 note, unlike the Quebec army bills, was payable in drafts on Quebec or Montreal. It bears a single signature, that of the Deputy Assistant Commissary General. There is a counterfoil at the left consisting of a patterned design rather than words.

$4

Face Design: No Vignettes	**Back Design:** Plain	
Colour: Black		
Issue Date: Partially Engraved _____181__ May 1 185	**Imprint:** None	
	Signature: mss. S.H. Monk	

Denom.	Issue Date	G	VG	F	VF	EF	Unc
$4	1815	VERY RARE – Estimate: $1,500. to $4.000.					

PROVINCIAL ISSUES
Alberta
PROSPERITY CERTIFICATE
REDEEMABLE 1936

Alberta's Social Credit government introduced "prosperity certificates" in 1936 in an attempt to alleviate the effects of the Great Depression. Every week the holder of a note had to affix a 1-cent stamp to the back to maintain its validity. The intended effect was to increase the velocity of circulation and discourage hoarding. As the end of each interval approached, the note holders spent their prosperity certificates in order to avoid having to purchase and affix the stamps. This obligation consequently often fell on the merchants. The government injected the prosperity certificates into circulation by using them to pay part of the salaries of the provincial civil servants. The original intention was that the notes would be redeemed by the provincial treasurer after two years, by which time 104 stamps would have been attached, yielding the government a small profit on the issue.

However the prosperity certificate experiment only lasted for about one year. The necessity for affixing 1-cent stamps was not popular, and to make matters worse the stamps kept falling off. The newspapers spearheaded a campaign to boycott the notes. Of the 357,680 prosperity certificates issued, all but 19,639 were redeemed.

A-1

Face Design: Provincial shield/lathework/provincial shield
Colour: Black with green tint

1 CENT	1 CENT	1 CENT	1 CENT	SEPT 16 1936	SEPT 23 1936	SEPT 30 1936	OCT 7 1936	OCT 14 1936	OCT 21 1936	OCT 28 1936	NOV 4 1936	NOV 12 1936	NOV 18 1936
NOV 25 1936	DEC 2 1936	DEC 9 1936	DEC 16 1936	DEC 23 1936	DEC 30 1936	JAN 6 1937	JAN 13 1937	JAN 20 1937	JAN 27 1937	FEB 3 1937	FEB 10 1937	FEB 17 1937	FEB 24 1937	MAR 3 1937
MAR 10 1937	MAR 17 1937	MAR 24 1937	MAR 31 1937	APRIL 7 1937	APRIL 14 1937	APRIL 21 1937	APRIL 28 1937	MAY 5 1937	MAY 12 1937	MAY 19 1937	MAY 26 1937	JUNE 2 1937	JUNE 9 1937	JUNE 16 1937
JUNE 23 1937	JUNE 30 1937	JULY 7 1937	JULY 14 1937	JULY 21 1937	JULY 28 1937	AUG 4 1937	AUG 11 1937	AUG 18 1937	AUG 25 1937	SEPT 1 1937	SEPT 8 1937	SEPT 15 1937	SEPT 22 1937	SEPT 29 1937
OCT 6 1937	OCT 13 1937	OCT 20 1937	OCT 27 1937	NOV 3 1937	NOV 10 1937	NOV 17 1937	NOV 24 1937	DEC 1 1937	DEC 8 1937	DEC 15 1937	DEC 22 1937	DEC 29 1937	JAN 5 1938	JAN 12 1938
JAN 19 1938	JAN 26 1938	FEB 2 1938	FEB 9 1938	FEB 16 1938	FEB 23 1938	MAR 2 1938	MAR 9 1938	MAR 16 1938	MAR 23 1938	MAR 30 1938	APRIL 6 1938	APRIL 13 1938	APRIL 20 1938	APRIL 27 1938
MAY 4 1938	MAY 11 1938	MAY 18 1938	MAY 25 1938	JUNE 1 1938	JUNE 8 1938	JUNE 15 1938	JUNE 22 1938	JUNE 29 1938	JULY 6 1938	JULY 13 1938	JULY 20 1938	JULY 27 1938	AUG 3 1938	

Back Design: Grid, with dated squares (varying numbers of green 1-cent stamps usually attached)
Colour: Black

Issue Date: August 5, 1936

Imprint: Western Printing & Lithographing Co. Ltd. Calgary

Signatures

Left: Engr. William Aberhart

Right: Engr. C. Cockroft
J.F. Percival in blue vertically.

Note: Certificates with a higher quantity of stamps on the back usually command a higher price.

Cat. No.	Denom.	Issue Date	G	VG	F	VF	EF	Unc
A-1	$1	1936	10.	20.	30.	50.	100.	250.

Colony of British Columbia
TREASURY NOTES

An issue of Treasury notes took place in 1862 to the amount of some $34,000 or £6,800 which consisted of 1,200 $25.00 notes, 200 $10.00 notes and 400 $5.00 notes. The attempt to circulate a Government paper currency failed and the notes were almost immediately withdrawn from circulation. The amount outstanding is only $40, apparently representing one of each denomination saved as specimens. (From "Treasury Notes of the Colony of British Columbia" by W. E. Ireland and R. A. Greene).

Cat. No.	Denom.	Issue Date	G	VG	F	VF	EF	Unc
BrC-1	$5	1862						
BrC-2	$10	1862		NONE KNOWN TO HAVE SURVIVED				
BrC-3	$25	1862						

New Brunswick
TREASURY NOTES

Unlike the other Maritime colonies, New Brunswick did not indulge extensively in the issue of treasury notes. Two small issues were released in 1805 and 1807 to cover a temporary shortfall in provincial revenue. These were redeemed in gold and silver, with interest.

ISSUE OF 1805		ISSUE OF 1807	
Denomination	Number Issued	Denomination	Number Issued
$4	900	$1	1,200
$6	600	$2	800
$8	600	$4	800
$10	400		
$20	200		

Cat. No.	Denom.	Issue Date	G	VG	F	VF	EF	Unc
NB-1	$4	1805						
NB-2	$6	1805						
NB-3	$8	1805		A $1 1807 TREASURY NOTE HELD				
NB-4	$10	1805		AT THE NEW BRUNSWICK MUSEUM,				
NB-5	$20	1805		OF THE REST NONE ARE KNOWN TO				
NB-6	$1	1807		HAVE SURVIVED.				
NB-7	$2	1807						
NB-8	$4	1807						

Until 1818 other provincial obligations called treasury warrants were issued to pay for the construction of roads and bridges. Since these had no specie backing, redemption was slow and difficult, and the warrants were discounted up to ten per cent when used in transactions. Treasury notes were again issued in 1818 to pay off the treasury warrants, but these too soon fell to a discount. The poor reputation of the provincial paper was cited as an argument against further issues which were proposed, in vain, from time to time until 1865.

Summary of Technical Details

Denomination	Number Authorized for Issue	Denomination	Number Authorized for Issue
5s. (currency)	2,000	£2	500
10s.	1,000	£2.10	1,000
£1	1,000	£3	400
£1.10	1,000	£5	260

(Denominations and quantities from *Money and Exchange in Canada to 1900*, by A. B. McCullough)

Cat. No.	Denom.	Issue Date	G	VG	F	VF	EF	Unc
NB-9	5s.	1818						
NB-10	10s.	1818						
NB-11	£1	1818						
NB-12	£1.10	1818			NONE KNOWN			
NB-13	£2	1818			TO HAVE SURVIVED			
NB-14	£2.10	1818						
NB-15	£3	1818						
NB-16	£5	1818						

NEWFOUNDLAND
GOVERNMENT TREASURY NOTES

Treasury notes were issued through the Newfoundland Savings Bank in 1834 in denominations of £25, £50 and £100 local sterling. These notes bore interest at 6% per annum. By 1836 all had been redeemed and destroyed.

The next issue was authorized in 1846, in denominations of £10, £25 and £50 local sterling, bearing interest at 5%. None are known to have survived. As these earlier notes were more like debentures (bonds), they are not given numbers.

Non-interest bearing treasury notes in denominations more suitable for general circulation were authorized in 1850. While denominations of £1, £5 and £10 currency were provided for under the act, only $1 notes (NF-1 type) are known to exist. The £1 notes were printed in sheets of four on paper watermarked "ISLAND OF NEWFOUNDLAND" at the centre of each note. The notes were to be signed by two treasury note commissioners as well as by the colonial treasurer. Twenty-three sheets of partially signed remainder notes, bearing the signatures of two treasury note commissioners only, have been found.

The treasury note act was amended in 1851 and again in 1855 under pressure from the British government, but no notes are known with these dates.

Number of notes authorized by Act of 1850 is as follows:
£1 currency — 16076; £5 currency — 1000; £10 currency — 200

NF-1

| Face Design: | —/sailing ships/— | Back Design: | Plain |
| Colour: | Black | | |

| Issue Date: | Partially Engraved ____18____ October 16, 1850 | Imprint: | Perkins, Bacon & Co. |

Signatures

Left: Any two: Wm. Thomas Lawrence O'Brien C.F. Bennett   **Right:** R. Carter

Cat. No.	Denom.	Variety	G	VG	F	VF	EF	Unc
NF-1	£1	Unsigned remainder	50.	100.	150.	275.	550.	1,100.
NF-1a	£1	Two signatures (at left), remainder	125.	250.	375.	650.	–	–
NF-1b	£1	Three signatures	350.	750.	1,150.	–	–	–

Note: Uncut pairs and sheets of four are known to exist.

Government Cash Notes

I. DEPARTMENT OF PUBLIC WORKS TYPE: 1901-1909

The "black and white" cash notes were designed to be a secure and prompt means of paying for materials and labour for road construction and maintenance. The notes were issued by the Department of Public Works, and bore the typed signatures of the Minister and Secretary of the Department. The notes were distributed as needed to each local road superintendant, whose manuscript signature at the lower centre was required to make the notes negotiable. The total issue in each fiscal year was limited to the amount voted by the legislature.

The fully completed cash notes were redeemable at the Bank of Montreal branches and charged against a special liquidation account held by the bank for the government. Upon presentation for payment, the notes were immediately removed from circulation and cancelled.

Summary of Technical Details

Year	Denomination				
	40c	50c	80c	$1	$5
1901	45,000	54,755	47,500	27,000	6,200
1902	17,500	15,000	65,000	50,000	5,000
1903	5,000	5,000	60,000	50,000	8,200
1904	5,000	5,000	59,896	57,500	8,000
1905	5,000	5,000	13,000	100,000	15,000
1906	1,990	2,000	4,994	49,992	25,000
1907	2,000	2,000	5,000	50,000	25,000
1908	2,000	2,000	5,000	50,000	25,000
1909	200	1,200	400	50,000	5,000

Total face value: $1,384,578.00

The numbers of notes issued do not necessarily reflect present-day availability. The $5 notes have virtually disappeared, while the lower values have had a slightly better rate of survival.

NF-2f

NF-3   **Photo Not Available**

NF-4b

NF-5a

NF-6h

The Following Design Applies To All Denominations
Only the Denomination Counters and Issue Dates Change

Face Design: Lathework and counters **Back Design:** Plain
/—/lathework & counters
Colour: Black, with year in red

Issue Date: Letterpress **Imprint:** American Bank Note
Year only, 1901 to 1909 Co. New York

Signatures

Left	**Lower Centre**	**Right**
Typed (1901-2) Geo. W. Mews	mss. various	Typed Geo. W. Gushue
(1903-4) James Harris		
(1905-9) M.T. Knight		

18

Cat. No.	Denom.	Issue Date	G	VG	F	VF	EF	Unc
NF-2a	40c	1901	60.	125.	200.	350.	700.	1,500.
NF-2b	40c	1902	60.	125.	200.	350.	700.	1,500.
NF-2c	40c	1903	60.	125.	200.	350.	700.	1,500.
NF-2d	40c	1904	60.	125.	200.	350.	700.	1,500.
NF-2e	40c	1905	60.	125.	200.	350.	700.	1,500.
NF-2f	40c	1906	60.	125.	200.	350.	700.	1,500.
NF-2g	40c	1907	60.	125.	200.	350.	700.	1,500.
NF-2h	40c	1908	60.	125.	200.	350.	700.	1,500.
NF-2i	40c	1909	125.	250.	350.	500.	1,100.	2,300.
NF-3a	50c	1901	60.	125.	200.	350.	700.	1,500.
NF-3b	50c	1902	60.	125.	200.	350.	700.	1,500.
NF-3c	50c	1903	60.	125.	200.	350.	700.	1,500.
NF-3d	50c	1904	60.	125.	200.	350.	700.	1,500.
NF-3e	50c	1905	60.	125.	200.	350.	700.	1,500.
NF-3f	50c	1906	60.	125.	200.	350.	700.	1,500.
NF-3g	50c	1907	60.	125.	200.	350.	700.	1,500.
NF-3h	50c	1908	60.	125.	200.	350.	700.	1,500.
NF-3i	50c	1909	75.	150.	250.	400.	800.	1,700.
NF-4a	80c	1901	100.	225.	350.	500.	900.	2,000
NF-4b	80c	1902	100.	225.	350.	500.	900.	2,000
NF-4c	80c	1903	100.	225.	350.	500.	900.	2,000
NF-4d	80c	1904	100.	225.	350.	500.	900.	2,000
NF-4e	80c	1905	100.	225.	350.	500.	900.	2,000
NF-4f	80c	1906	100.	225.	350.	500.	900.	2,000
NF-4g	80c	1907	100.	225.	350.	500.	900.	2,000
NF-4h	80c	1908	100.	225.	350.	500.	900.	2,000
NF-4i	80c	1909	125.	300.	450.	700.	1,500.	3,000
NF-5a	$1	1901	100.	225.	350.	500.	900.	2,000.
NF-5b	$1	1902	100.	225.	350.	500.	900.	2,000.
NF-5c	$1	1903	100.	225.	350.	500.	900.	2,000.
NF-5d	$1	1904	100.	225.	350.	500.	900.	2,000.
NF-5e	$1	1905	100.	225.	350.	500.	900.	2,000.
NF-5f	$1	1906	100.	225.	350.	500.	900.	2,000.
NF-5g	$1	1907	100.	225.	350.	500.	900.	2,000.
NF-5h	$1	1908	100.	225.	350.	500.	900.	2,000.
NF-5i	$1	1909	100.	225.	350.	500.	900.	2,000.
NF-6a	$5	1901	300.	600.	1,000.	1,500.	3,000.	6,500.
NF-6b	$5	1902	300.	600.	1,000.	1,500.	3,000.	6,500.
NF-6c	$5	1903	300.	600.	1,000.	1,500.	3,000.	6,500.
NF-6d	$5	1904	300.	600.	1,000.	1,500.	3,000.	6,500.
NF-6e	$5	1905	300.	600.	1,000.	1,500.	3,000.	6,500.
NF-6f	$5	1906	300.	600.	1,000.	1,500.	3,000.	6,500.
NF-6g	$5	1907	300.	600.	1,000.	1,500.	3,000.	6,500.
NF-6h	$5	1908	300.	600.	1,000.	1,500.	3,000.	6,500.
NF-6i	$5	1909	300.	600.	1,000.	1,500.	3,000.	6,500.

II. DOUBLE DATE MULTICOLOURED TYPE: 1910-1914

In 1910 the Newfoundland government enacted legislation extending the use of cash notes to other departments. Besides paying for the construction and maintenance of roads, the new type cash notes were used for welfare payments and marine works.

These notes bore two consecutive years, printed in red ink, corresponding to the government's fiscal year. They were signed by the colonial secretary and minister of finance. The third signature, formerly applied by hand to the earlier type of cash notes, was omitted. The notes were printed by Whitehead, Morris & Co. Ltd., of London, England, in denominations of 25c, 50c, $1, $2 and $5, with tints of various colours for each denomination.

As before, the notes were withdrawn from circulation and cancelled upon presentation for payment at the Bank of Montreal. The cancelled notes were destroyed in the presence of the auditor general. The issue of cash notes was not continued beyond 1914. Cheques and stocks of surplus silver coin took their place, although these forms of payment were not always as convenient as the cash notes.

Two basic varieties occur. The 1910-11 notes have lathework "scallop" design in the upper right corner. This was replaced on later issues by a denominational counter. Other accompanying changes were made. On the 1910-11 notes, the "word" form of the denomination found below the vignette is partially covered by the tint, while on later issues the tint is clear of the value.

Quantities of Notes Issued by Denomination and Fiscal Year

Fiscal Year	Denomination				
	25c	50c	$1	$2	$5
1910-11	10,000	7,000	56,000	10,000	37,000
1911-12	8,000	20,700	73,000	29,000	35,000
1912-13	20,750	81,250	171,700	22,000	25,800
1913-14	12,000	20,000	44,000	19,500	15,800

Total face value: $1,150,862.50

The lower denominations are now more frequently encountered, having been kept as mementoes.

NF-7a

1910-1911 Issues

All denominations have a "scallop" design in upper right corner.

NF-9c

1911-1914 Issues

All denominations have a "counter" in upper right corner.

NF-7c

Face Design: —/waterfall/—
Colour: Black with dull red and grey-brown tints.

NF-7c

Back Design: Lathework and counter
Colour: Ochre ends, blue centre, grey diagonal shading.

NF-8d

Face Design: —/waterfall/—
Colour: Black with dull red and grey-brown tints.

NF-8c

Back Design: Lathework and counter
Colour: Dull red, brown and grey diagonal shading.

NF-9d

Face Design: —/waterfall/—
    Colour: Black with bright green, dull red and grey-brown tints.

NF-9d

Back Design: Lathework and counter
    Colour: Dull rose red ends, green centre, peripheral grey diagonal shading.

NF-10b

Face Design: —/waterfall/—
    Colour: Black with yellow, grey-blue and grey-brown tints.

NF-10b

Back Design: Lathework and counter
Colour: Grey-blue ends, ochre centre, grey-brown diagonal shading.

NF-11a

Face Design: —/waterfall/—
Colour: Black with blue and grey tints, dull red at ends and light yellow centre.

NF-11a

Back Design: Lathework and counter
Colour: Green and blue ends, dull red centre, grey-brown diagonal shading.

Issue Date: 1910-11
1911-12
1912-13
1913-14

Imprint: Whitehead, Morris & Co. Ltd. Engravers, London

Cat. No.	Denom.	Issue Date	G	VG	F	VF	EF	Unc
NF-7a	25c	1910-11	15.	30.	60.	120.	250.	625.
NF-7b	25c	1911-12	15.	30.	60.	120.	250.	625.
NF-7c	25c	1912-13	15.	30.	60.	120.	250.	625.
NF-7d	25c	1913-14	15.	30.	60.	120.	250.	625.
NF-8a	50c	1910-11	20.	40.	80.	160.	325.	800.
NF-8b	50c	1911-12	20.	40.	80.	160.	325.	800.
NF-8c	50c	1912-13	20.	40.	80.	160.	325.	800.
NF-8d	50c	1913-14	20.	40.	80.	160.	325.	800.
NF-9a	$1	1910-11	50.	100.	200.	350.	700.	1,750.
NF-9b	$1	1911-12	50.	100.	200.	350.	700.	1,750.
NF-9c	$1	1912-13	50.	100.	200.	350.	700.	1,750.
NF-9d	$1	1913-14	50.	100.	200.	350.	700.	1,750.
NF-10a	$2	1910-11	350.	700.	1,050.	1,825.	3,700.	7,500.
NF-10b	$2	1911-12	350.	700.	1,050.	1,825.	3,700.	7,500.
NF-10c	$2	1912-13	350.	700.	1,050.	1,825.	3,700.	7,500.
NF-10d	$2	1913-14	350.	700.	1,050.	1,825.	3,700.	7,500.
NF-11a	$5	1910-11	400.	800.	1,200.	2,100.	4,200.	10,500.
NF-11b	$5	1911-12	400.	800.	1,200.	2,100.	4,200.	10,500.
NF-11c	$5	1912-13	400.	800.	1,200.	2,100.	4,200.	10,500.
NF-11d	$5	1913-14	400.	800.	1,200.	2,100.	4,200.	10,500.

Treasury Notes of 1920

Treasury notes in $1 and $2 denominations dated 1920 were issued to deal with a shortage of silver coin (precipitated in part by the withdrawal of the cash notes) at a time when the price of silver was very high on world markets.

Two tints, four face plates and four back plates were engraved for the $1 denomination, two tints, two face plates and two back plates for the $2 denomination. There were no check letters, the notes being numbered serially. All notes printed were in series A, which is shown by the letter A prefixing the number.

The "Admiral" portrait of King George V on the left of the $1 note was the same as the one used on the centre of the 1911 $1,000 Canadian Dominion notes.

Of the $1,200,000 worth of these notes printed, $1,181,704 had been destroyed by Dec. 8, 1939. This amount includes both stocks of unissued notes and notes withdrawn from circulation. Small additional quantities were subsequently redeemed leaving an outstanding total of about $12,000 face value.

Summary of Technical Details for 1920 Issues

Cat. No.	Denom.	Series	Serial Numbers	Quantities Printed	Quantities Issued
NF-12	$1	A	000001-600000	600,000	407,000
NF-13	$2	A	000001-300000	300,000	261,000

NF-12

Face Design: "Admiral" portrait of King George V/—/caribou head
Colour: Black with blue tint.

NF-12

Back Design: —/Official seal of Newfoundland, supported by ship and anchor/—
Colour: Blue.

NF-13

Face Design: —/mining scene/caribou head
Colour: Black with light brown tint.

NF-13

Back Design: —/Official Seal of Newfoundland, supported by ship and anchor/—
Colour: Brown

Issue Date: Engr. Jany 2nd, 1920
Company, Ottawa

Imprint: American Bank Note

Signatures

Left: mss. C.F. Renouf
mss. F.A. Hickey
mss. G.W. Bursell
mss. J.S. Keating

Right: Typed, H.J. Brownrigg
Typed, H.J. Brownrigg
Typed, H.J. Brownrigg
Typed, H.J. Brownrigg

Cat. No.	Denom.	Issue Date	G	VG	F	VF	EF	Unc
NF-12	$1	1920	35.	75.	115.	200.	400.	1,000.
NF-13	$2	1920	70.	150.	225.	400.	1,000.	2,500.

PROVINCE OF NOVA SCOTIA

Treasury Notes

I. TREASURY RECEIPTS 1763-1782

The Nova Scotia colonial government frequently found its supply of specie inadequate for its needs. It then appealed to the wealthier citizens to bring in their silver and gold to the treasury, in return for which they would receive treasury receipts payable at a future date and bearing six per cent annual interest in the meantime. Originally issued only for various larger sums, these debenture-like documents soon assumed a currency function, which led to their being issued for more suitable amounts such as 10 shillings and 20 shillings currency. In 1765 legislation was enacted to provide for the exchange of large denominations for smaller ones. From 1773 they could be made payable either to the bearer or to the original recipient, at his discretion. In 1776 all old interest-bearing treasury receipts (as well as treasury warrants, a form of promissory note used by the government to pay for supplies and services) were called in and exchanged for new notes.

None of these early notes are known to have survived, and they were not specifically issued for currency purposes, so catalogue numbers are not assigned to them.

II. PROVINCIAL TREASURY NOTES-1812

The first treasury notes, issued specifically for circulation were authorized in 1812 to the extent of £12,000 cy. Five copper plates were engraved in denominations of £1, £2.10, £5, £12.50, and £50 (a £20 denomination was authorized but not used). The notes were printed locally, and although the treasury note commissioners thought the cost was excessive, no competing printers could be found.

These are the only treasury notes to bear interest, which was paid at six per cent per annum. For this reason the government was unusually keen to have them withdrawn and cancelled over the next few years. Once redeemed at the treasury, notes of this issue were not reissuable, but were cancelled and destroyed.

The original plates are still in the possession of the Province of Nova Scotia, and a few reprints were made early in the twentieth century.

£2.10 Issue – 1812

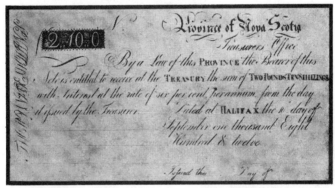

NS-2

Face Design: Wording only
Colour: Black

Back Design: Plain

Issue Date: Engr. (September 10, 1812)

Imprint: None

Signatures

Left: mss. John Black
mss. Law. Hartshorne
mss. James Foreman

Right: mss. Mich. Wallace

Cat. No.	Denom.	Issue Date	G	VG	F	VF	EF	Unc
NS-1	£1	1812						
NS-2	£2.10	1812	ISSUED (FULLY SIGNED AND DATED)					
NS-3	£5	1812	TREASURY NOTES OF 1812 TO 1838 ARE					
NS-4	£12.10	1812	EXTREMELY RARE. Estimate: G-$1,000. to VG-$3,000.					
NS-5	£50	1812						

III. NON-INTEREST BEARING ISSUE 1813-1817

Two copper plates were engraved for the printing of £1 and £2 non-interest bearing treasury notes which were issued in 1813 and 1814. These were issued in large quantity to replace the 1812 interest-bearing notes, and a total issue of £20,000 was authorized. A further issue of £5 notes was made in 1817, but some were antedated 1813.

These notes were fundable; that is, if they were presented at the treasury and specie was unavailable, they could be exchanged in multiples of £100 for interest-bearing provincial securities. The £1 and £2 notes could be reissued when received by the treasury. Reprints exist.

Summary of Technical Details

Denomination	Quantity Printed	Amount (Hfx. currency)
£1	14,000	£14,000
£2	3,000	£ 6,000
£5	1,000	£ 5,000

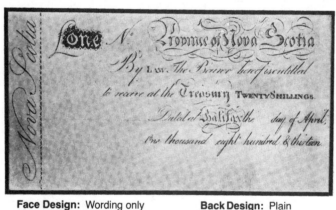

NS-6

Face Design: Wording only
Colour: Black

Back Design: Plain

Issue Date: Partially Engraved
    _____April 1813
    £1, £2 April 30, 1813
    £5   April 30, 1813

Imprint: None

Signatures

Left: mss. John Black
    mss. Law. Hartshorne
    mss. James Foreman

Right: mss. Mich. Wallace

Cat. No.	Denom.	Issue Date	G	VG	F	VF	EF	Unc
NS-6	£1	1813	ISSUED (FULLY SIGNED AND DATED)					
NS-7	£2	1813	TREASURY NOTES OF 1812 TO 1838 ARE					
NS-8	£5	1813-17	EXTREMELY RARE: G-$1,000. to VG-$3,000.					

IV. ISSUES OF 1817-1823

A new £15,000 issue consisting of £1, £2 and £5 notes, in unknown proportions, was authorized in 1818 but dated April 20, 1817. A further £10,000 was authorized in 1819, £20,000 more in 1820 and £5,000 in 1823. The notes were printed in Boston.

NS-9

Face Design: Wording only	**Back Design:** Plain
Colour: Black	

Issue Date: Partially Engraved	**Imprint:** None
_____18__	
April 20, 1817	
June 1, 1820	
January 1, 1821	
July 2, 1821	
June 1, 1823 and	
possibly others	

Signatures

Left: mss. Wm. Lawson   **Right:** mss. Mich. Wallace
mss. J. Foreman

Cat. No.	Denom.	Issue Date	G	VG	F	VF	EF	Unc
NS-9	£1	1817-23	ISSUED (FULLY SIGNED AND DATED)					
NS-10	£2	1817-23	TREASURY NOTES OF 1812 TO 1838 ARE					
NS-11	£5	1817-21	EXTREMELY RARE: G-$1,000. to VG-$3,000.					

V. THE DOLLAR ISSUE OF 1820

Notes of 5 shillings and 10 shillings currency (equivalent to $1 and $2) were authorized to the extent of £8,000 by an act of 1821. However, the notes of these denominations which have turned up are dated September 5, 1820. They are hand-drawn counterfeits, bearing the (forged) signature of the provincial treasurer only. The note shown below is one such counterfeit.

NS-13

Face Design: Wording only
Colour: Black

Back Design: Plain

Issue Date	Imprint	Signatures
mss. September 5, 1820	None	mss. Mich. Wallace

Cat. No.	Denom.	Issue Date	G	VG	F	VF	EF	Unc
NS-12	$1	1820	ISSUED (FULLY SIGNED AND DATED)					
NS-13	$2	1820	TREASURY NOTES OF 1812 TO 1838 ARE EXTREMELY RARE: G-$1,000. to VG-$3,000.					

VI. ENGRAVED ISSUES OF 1824-ca. 1832

The £1 and £2 plates used for printing treasury notes in Boston until 1823 were sent to the province's agents Smith, Forsyth & Co., in Liverpool, England, in 1824. A new £5 plate had to be prepared in England, the old one having been lost. A large number of notes, consisting of £1, £2 and £5 denominations, was prepared, and these were probably issued over a number of years, with various dates. In 1829 the addition of the 10 shilling denomination was authorized and was probably printed by an English firm, dated 1830. More 10 shilling notes were provided for by an act of 1832 and 5 shilling notes also entered circulation about the same time. At least some of the plates still exist.

Summary of Technical Details

Denomination	Date	Quantity Printed	Amount (Hfx.currency)
5s ($1)	1830-ca. 1832	3,900	£ 975
10s ($2)	1830-ca. 1832	3,000	£ 1,500
£1	1824-	40,000	£40,000
£2	1824-	15,000	£30,000
£5	1824-	2,000	£10,000

NS-15

Face Design: Wording only	**Back Design:** Plain
Issue Date: 10s: Partially engraved _____1, 1830 5s., £1, £2, £5: uncertain	**Imprint:** None

Signatures

Left: mss. vaious (two)

Right: mss. Mich. Wallace or Charles W. Wallace

Cat. No.	Denom.	Issue Date	G	VG	F	VF	EF	Unc
NS-14	5s.($1)	1830-ca. 1832						
NS-15	10s.($2)	1830-ca. 1832						
NS-16	£1	1824-			ISSUED (FULLY SIGNED AND DATED)			
NS-17	£2	1824-			TREASURY NOTES OF 1812 TO 1838 ARE			
NS-18	£5	1824-			EXTREMELY RARE: G-$1,000. to VG-$3,000.			

VII. LITHOGRAPHIC ISSUE 1825-ca. 1832

These notes are characterized by large oblong shapes in blue or black ink in the centre of the notes, in which the printed details appear in white letters. They were printed by Peter Maverick of New York. At least two modifications of the design exist.

FIRST ISSUE

NS-19

Face Design: Thistle/"scalloped" centre block/floral panel with small crown
Colour: Black

Back Design: Plain

SECOND ISSUE

NS-20

Face Design: —/oval centre block. floral panel with large crown
Colour: Black or blue

Back Design: Plain

	Issue Date:	Partially Engraved:		Imprint:	1825: Peter Maverick
		_____ 18__			1829-32: D. Henderson
		August 1, 1825			
		June 1, 1829			
		January 1, 1831			
		March 1, 1832			

Signatures

Left: mss. various (two or three) Right: mss. Mich. Wallace or Charles W. Wallace

Cat. No.	Denom.	Issue Date	G	VG	F	VF	EF	Unc
NS-19	£1	1825			ISSUED (FULLY SIGNED AND DATED)			
NS-20	£1	1828-32			TREASURY NOTES OF 1812 TO 1838 ARE			
					EXTREMELY RARE: Estimate: G-$1,000. to VG-$3,000.			

VIII. RAWDON, WRIGHT & HATCH ISSUE 1838

A new issue of 8,000 £1 notes, prepared from a 4/on steel plate, was prepared in 1838, replacing earlier notes as they became too worn or soiled for further use. By this time chartered banking was well established in Nova Scotia, and the banks were prohibited from issuing their own notes in denominations of less than £5 currency, to prevent bank notes from competing with the provincial notes.

PHOTO NOT AVAILABLE

NS-21

Face Design: Floral panel/Royal crest/scrollwork panel Back Design: Plain

Colour: Black

Issue Date	Imprint	Signatures
Engraved___18__	Rawdon, Wright & Hatch	Unknown

Cat. No.	Denom.	Issue Date	G	VG	F	VF	EF	Unc
					ISSUED (FULLY SIGNED AND DATED)			
NS-21	£1	1838			TREASURY NOTES OF 1812 TO 1838 ARE			
					EXTREMELY RARE: Estimate: G-$1,000. to VG-$3,000.			

IX. PERKINS, BACON AND PETCH ISSUE 1846-1854

All old issues of treasury notes were withdrawn in the late 1840's and replaced by notes of the £1 denomination only. Sixty thousand of these were printed initially. A subsequent printing with the date engraved became the first treasury notes of the province to be numbered by machine. Those of later dates were used to pay for railroad construction.

NS-22

Face Design:	3/4 length portrait of Queen Victoria (Chalon) /Royal Crest/—	**Back Design:**	Plain
Colour:	Black		
Issue Date:	Partially Engraved: _____18__ The first day of August 1846 May 1, 1848 June 1, 1853 or Engr. The first day of June 1854	**Imprint:**	Perkins, Bacon & Petch

Signatures

Left: mss. various   **Right:** (two) mss. various

Cat. No.	Denom.	Issue Date	G	VG	F	VF	EF	Unc
NS-22	£1	1846-54	250.	500.	750.	1,300.	2,600.	6,500.

Listed prices are for WHOLE NOTES. Notes which have been CANCELLED by cutting out the signatures are worth 25% of price.

X. DECIMAL CURRENCY ISSUES 1861-1866

Nova Scotia adopted decimal currency in 1860. All subsequent treasury notes were issued in the denomination of $5 (Nova Scotia currency) only. The previous £1 treasury notes were equivalent to $4. After Confederation all treasury notes were to be withdrawn and destroyed. By 1875 only $46,194 remained outstanding of a total circulation of $622,458.

NS-23

Face Design: Queen Victoria (Winterhalter portrait)/shield and Indian/Prince of Wales
Colour: Black with green tint

NS-23

Back Design: —/St. George slaying dragon/—
Colour: Orange

Issue Date: Engraved
June 1, 1861
May 1, 1865
May 1, 1866
Aug. 1, 1866

Imprint: American Bank Note Company, New York

Signatures
Left: miss. various (two)
Right: mss. J.H. Anderson or James McNab

Cat. No.	Denom.	Issue Date	G	VG	F	VF	EF	Unc
NS-23	$5	1861-66	400.	800.	1,200.	2,100.	4,200.	10,500.

Listed prices are for WHOLE NOTES. Notes which have been CANCELLED by cutting out the signatures are worth 25% of price.

PRINCE EDWARD ISLAND

Treasury Notes

I. ISLAND OF ST. JOHN ISSUE 1790

Known as Island of St. John until 1799, Prince Edward Island had become a separate colony from Nova Scotia in 1769. Trade was conducted by a primitive means of barter until 1790, when provincial treasury notes were issued to provide a circulating medium. The notes were used to pay for public works, and were receivable for taxes and duties.

The first issue consisted of a total of £500 P.E.I. Currency, to be redeemed in three years. The enabling legislation was passed by the General Assembly on November 20, 1790, and this is the date printed on the notes. The notes carry the warning "Death to Counterfeit" vertically at the right end.

Summary of Technical Details

Denomination	Dated	Quantity Printed	Amount (Currency)
1s.	1790	500	£ 25
1s.3d.	1790	480	£ 30
2s.6d.	1790	480	£ 60
5s.	1790	500	£125
10s.	1790	100	£ 50
20s.	1790	110	£110
40s.	1790	50	£100

PEI-3

Face Design: Pattern of leaves and scrollwork margins

Colour: Black

Back Design: Plain

Issue Date: Engr. Nov. 20, 1790

Imprint: None

Signatures

Left: mss Robert Gray

Right: mss: Peter J. Stewart and Joseph Robinson

Cat. No.	Denom.	Issue Date	G	VG	F	VF	EF	Unc
PEI-1	1s.	1790	480.	900.	1,500.	2,000.	2,500.	5,000.
PEI-2	1s.3d.	1790	480.	900.	1,500.	2,000.	2,500.	5,000.
PEI-3	2s.6d.	1790	480.	900.	1,500.	2,000.	2,500.	5,000.
PEI-4	5s.	1790	480.	900.	1,500.	2,000.	2,500.	5,000.
PEI-5	10s.	1790	480.	900.	1,500.	2,000.	2,500.	5,000.
PEI-6	20s.	1790	480.	900.	1,500.	2,000.	2,500.	5,000.
PEI-7	40s.	1790	480.	900.	1,500.	2,000.	2,500.	5,000.

II. ISSUES OF 1825-1834

The Legislature of Prince Edward Island authorized the second issue of provincial treasury notes in 1825. Originally consisting of an issue of £5000 currency in £1, £2 and £5 notes, a 10 shilling denomination was subsequently added at the insistence of the merchants, to the extent of an additional £800.

Three treasury note commissioners were appointed to procure and sign the notes and to superintend their circulation. All notes of the issue were to be given the same date. The provincial treasurer countersigned the notes prior to issue. The notes could be reissued by the treasury. If they were presented for payment when no specie was available (the usual situation), they could be exchanged for interest-bearing "funding certificates". The islanders seemed to accept the notes readily enough, for none were presented for funding over the next decade. Originally the notes were supposed to be withdrawn and redeemed after three years but the authorizing act was repeatedly renewed for several years at a time whenever the redemption date drew near.

The notes were very plain, with the following format:

"No.____Prince Edward Island/
Charlotte Town, 1825/
By Law, the bearer of this note is entitled/
to receive at the Treasury the/
sum of (   )".

In 1830 and again in 1831 it was represented that the volume of treasury notes in circulation was inadequate, and in each case the circulation was expanded by an additional £3000 cy. In 1833 a further issue of £5000 was enacted and put in circulation the following year, with the provision that £1000 be withdrawn and redeemed at the end of each year after the date of issue, for five years.

The redemption process was suspended at first, but the required total redemption of £5000 was carried out at the insistance of the British Colonial Office, which took a dim view of the ever increasing irredeemable circulation and consequent public debt. By 1839 the total circulation had been reduced from £16,800 to £11,800, only to make room for treasury warrants, irredeemable notes of small denomination which bore interest at six per cent. There were three unfortunate results of such a currency. In accordance with Gresham's law, "bad money drives out good", there was no metallic currency on the island. Shopkeepers resorted to dispensing alcoholic libations in lieu of small change. The establishment of chartered banking facilities in the colony was discouraged. The currency itself became increasingly inflated, so that by 1839, 20 shillings sterling equalled 30 shillings P.E.I. currency.

Summary of Technical Details

Denomination	Date*	Quantity Printed	Amount (PEI Currency)
10s.	1825	1,600	£ 800
£1	1825	1,700 (est.)	£1,700
£2	1825	900 (est.)	£1,800
£5	1825	300 (est.)	£1,500
5s.	1830	2,000 (est.)	£ 500
10s.	1830	3,000 (est.)	£1,500
£1	1830	1,000 (est.)	£1,000
5s.	1831	2,000	£ 500
10s.	1831	3,000	£1,500
£1	1831	1,000	£1,000
5s.	1833	2,000	£ 500
10s.	1833	1,000	£ 500
£1	1833	1,000	£1,000
£2	1833	1,000	£2,000
£5	1833	200	£1,000

* The date listing refers to the date of passage of the authorizing legislation, and the notes may not have entered circulation until the following year. The issue authorized under the act of 1833 is believed to have been dated 1834.

PHOTO NOT AVAILABLE

Face Design: Presumed to have no vignette

Colour: Black

Back Design: Plain

Issue Date	Imprint	Signatures
Uncertain	Unknown	mss. various

Cat. No.	Denom.	Issue Date	G	VG	F	VF	EF	Unc
PEI-8	5s.	1830-34						
PEI-9	10s.	1825-34						
PEI-10	£1	1825-34		NO NOTES KNOWN TO HAVE SURVIVED				
PEI-11	£2	1825-34						
PEI-12	£5	1825-34						

III. ISSUES OF 1848-1870

The Legislature attempted to issue a further £15,000 in treasury notes in 1845, to be redeemed in fifteen years. This was to be in addition to the £11,800 still in circulation. The Colonial Office adamantly refused to permit it, and was not swayed by offers to limit the issue to £10,000 payable in ten years. A request for a loan of £12,000 sterling to back a redeemable treasury note issue was likewise rejected in 1848. In the early 1850's the prosperity of the colony and growing government revenues permitted the redemption of a large part of the old treasury notes still in circulation. With confidence restored, new issues were circulated over the period 1851 to 1870. The numbers issued have not been determined.

PEI-13

Face Design: —/sailing ship/seal on ice floe **Back Design:** Plain
Colour: Black

PEI-14

Face Design: —/Farmer ploughing with team of horses/ shipbuilding **Back Design:** Plain
Colour: Black

PEI-15

Face Design: **Farmer mowing hay/ Royal Crest/sheaf of grain**

Colour: Black

Back Design: Plain

PEI-16

Face Design: —/Provincial Legislature Building/—

Colour: Black

Back Design: Plain

PEI-17

Face Design: —/Provincial Seal/—

Back Design: **Plain**

Issue Date: Partially Engraved:
_____18_:
Jan. 1, 1848
Jan. 27, 1855
July 23, 1858
1866:
Sept. 12, 1868
Mar. 9, 1870

Imprint: Warrington (1848-58)
or Warrington and
American Bank Note Co.
Logo (1858-70)

Signatures: mss. various

Cat. No.	Denom.	Issue Date	G	VG	F	VF	EF	Unc
PEI-13	5s.	1848-1870	400.	800.	1,200.	2,100.	4,200.	8,500.
PEI-14	10s.	1848-1870	400.	800.	1,200.	2,100.	4,200.	8,500.
PEI-15	£1	1848-1870	500.	1,000.	1,500.	2,600.	5.200.	10,500.
PEI-16	£2	1848-1870	500.	1,000.	1,500.	2,600.	5,200.	10,500.
PEI-17	£5	1848-1870	500.	1,000.	1,500.	2,600.	5,200.	10,500.

*Note: These treasury notes are usually found cancelled, with number, date and signature inked out. Prices are for cancelled notes.

IV. DOLLAR ISSUE OF 1872

Prince Edward Island adopted decimal currency in 1871, the last of the colonies now comprising Canada to do so. A new issue of treasury notes in $10 and $20 denominations was released to replace the former notes expressed in pounds and shillings. An extravagantly meandering railroad had been built, greatly increasing public debt, and the colony joined Confederation in 1873 as an alternative to insolvency. Treasury notes were then called in and redeemed, after only a small quantity of notes of the 1872 issue had been put into circulation.

PEI-18

Face Design: Prince Arthur/seal, Royal Crest/Britannia seated
Colour: Black with green tint

PEI-18

Back Design: Lathework and counters
Colour: Green

PEI-19

Face Design: Agricultural implements/seal, Royal Crest/sailor on dock
Colour: Black with green tint

PEI-19

Back Design: Lathework and counters
Colour: Green

Issue Date: Engraved: January 2, 1872	**Imprint:** British American Bank Note Co.
Signatures	
Left: mss. various	**Right:** mss. various mss. various

Cat. No.	Denom.	Issue Date	G	VG	F	VF	EF	Unc
PEI-18	$10	1872	600.	1,200.	1,800.	3,150.	6,300.	15,750.
PEI-19	$20	1872	600.	1,200.	1,800.	3,150.	6,300.	15,750.

UPPER CANADA
Provisional Government Notes of 1837

Following the collapse of the 1837 Rebellion in Upper Canada, its leader, William Lyon Mackenzie, fled with some of his supporters to New York State. He then set up a "provisional government" on Navy Island, a small island in the Niagara River about three miles above the falls. The island was used as a base for predatory raids against the Canadian mainland. Mackenzie issued scrip when all other means of acquiring supplies failed. The notes were allegedly payable four months after date at City Hall, Toronto, and were based on nothing more substantial than the dream of a successful invasion of Upper Canada.

In a desparate bid to make his scrip more appealing to the business community of Buffalo, Mackenzie had the signature of David Gibson forged on the notes. Gibson, a prominent and wealthy man, had been one of Mackenzie's supporters but at the time the scrip bearing his name was issued, he was a hunted fugitive, with a £500 bounty on his head, hiding under a straw-stack near Oshawa. The forgery was in vain, for the notes never circulated to a significant extent. In fact, the scrip was ridiculed on both sides of the border. Finally Mackenzie, finding no other use for his paper pledges, used the notes as wrappers for his newspapers.

UC-3a

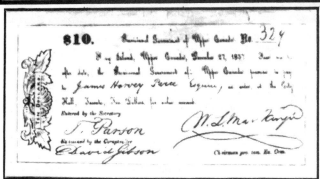

UC-3b

Face Design: Floral scroll work/—/—		**Back Design:** Plain	
Colour: Black, with light blue tint			
Issue Date: Engr.: Dec. 27, 1837		**Imprint:** None	
Signatures			
Left: mss. T. Parson or P.H. Watson; David Gibson (forged)		**Right:** mss. Wm. L. Mackenzie	

Cat. No.	Denom.	Issue Date	Variety	G	VG	F	VF	EF	Unc
UC-1	$1	1837	–						
UC-2	$2	1837	–		Estimate: $2,000. to $5,000.				
UC-3a	$10	1837	Large Letters						
UC-3b	$10	1837	Small Letters						

MUNICIPAL ISSUES

Although the redeemable status of these municipal notes is questionable, the majority are scarce and have considerable value. Some are actually debentures (similar to bonds). The listings are alphabetical according to city.

Brockville

THE MUNICIPAL COUNCIL OF THE
UNITED COUNTIES OF LEEDS AND GRENVILLE

The United Counties of Leeds and Grenville issued £25 (currency) debentures in the early 1850's, which bore six per cent annual interest paid twice yearly. Although these securities had the appearance and dimensions of bank notes, it is doubtful whether they circulated to a very great extent because of their large denomination. Interest payments are usually found recorded on the back. The debentures were pen cancelled.

MU-1

Face Design: —/Royal Crest/—	**Back Design:** Plain
Colour: Black	

Issue Date: Partially Engraved:	**Imprint:** Rawdon, Wright, Hatch
———18—	& Edson, New York
12th Dec'r 1850	
July 9, 1850	
July 2nd, 1851	
Jan. 8, 1852	
Feb. 14, 1852	

Signatures

Left	Centre	Right
mss. J.L. Schofield	mss. James Jessup	mss. George Sherwood

Cat. No.	Denom.	Issue Date	VG	F	VF	EF	Unc
MU-1	£25 ($100)	1850-52	5.	8.	13.	26.	65.

Cobourg

Board of Police

These notes were repayable one year after date, with interest. Both issues are usually found pen cancelled.

I. COAT OF ARMS TYPE
1848

MU-2

MU-3

Face Design: Woman seated at dockside/Royal Crest; small steamboat below/ women seated at dockside	**Back Design:** Plain	
Colour: Black		
Issue Date: Partially Engraved: _____184_ 1848: various, May or earlier	**Imprint:** None	

Signatures

Left: mss. David Brodie **Right:** mss. Asa A. Burnham

Cat. No.	Denom.	Issue Date	G	VG	F	VF	EF	Unc
MU-2	5s.($1)	1848	25.	50.	75.	125.	250.	625.
MU-3	10s.($2)	1848	25.	50.	75.	125.	250.	625.

II. SAILING SHIPS TYPE
1848

MU-4

MU-5

Face Design: —/sailing ships/—		**Back Design:** Plain
Colour: Black		

Issue Date: Partially Engraved: _____184_ 1848: various, Oct. to Dec.		**Imprint:** Star Office

Signatures

Left: mss. David Brodie   **Right:** mss. Asa A. Burnham

Cat. No.	Denom.	Issue Date	G	VG	F	VF	EF	Unc
MU-4	5s.($1)	1848	15.	30.	45.	80.	150.	375.
MU-5	10s.($2)	1848	15.	30.	45.	80.	150.	375.

Guelph

DISTRICT OF WELLINGTON

These crudely produced notes were repayable in varying numbers of years after date, with interest. They were issued in connection with road construction. Many of the notes were used to pay the labourers, a purpose for which the 5s. denomination was suitably chosen. The notes are usually pen cancelled.

MU-6

Face Design: Cherub/Duke of Wellington, on horse-back/—
Colour: Black

Back Design: Plain

Issue Date: Partially Engraved: _____18__
1 Dec'r 1848

Imprint: Fell, Hamilton

Signatures
Left: mss. James Wright

Right: mss. Wm. Stewart

Cat. No.	Denom.	Issue Date	VG	F	VF	EF	Unc
MU-6	5s. ($1)	1848	5.	10.	18.	35.	85.

Hamilton

These notes were repayable twelve months after date, with interest. They feature medallion engraving above and below the portraits. Different check letters were used for each year of issue, a peculiarity shared with the notes of the Corporation of the City of Toronto. The check letters of the surviving notes suggest that the notes may have been issued annually from 1848 until at least 1861, but only those known to exist are listed.

MU-7

MU-8

Face Design: Queen Victoria (Chalon portrait)/crest/Prince Consort **Back Design:** Plain
Colour: Black

Issue Date: Sept. 1, 1855
Apr. 1, 1856
1859:
June 1, 1860
1861:

Imprint: Rawdon, Wright, Hatch & Edson (American Bank Note Co. logo added after 1858)

Signatures
Left: mss. Robt. M. Kerr **Right:** mss. Various

Cat. No.	Denom.	Issue Date	G	VG	F	VF	EF	Unc
MU-7	$1 (5s.)	1855-61	150.	300.	450.	800.	1,600.	4,000.
MU-8	$2 (10s)	1855-61	150.	300.	450.	800.	1,600.	4,000.

Kingston

I. COMMONALTY OF KINGSTON ISSUE 1842

The Town of Kingston issued a total of £2,000 currency in 5 shilling and 10 shilling notes in 1842 to help meet the cost of an ambitious programme of public works. A red "City of Kingston" seal (often found badly faded) was stamped at the lower right. The notes bore interest and were repayable after one year, but were not uniformly well received by the townsfolk. In 1846, when the town had amassed such a debt load that no further accommodation from the banks was obtainable, a further issue of £5,000 was proposed but had to be abandoned in the face of strong opposition.

MU-9

MU-10

Face Design: —/view of Kingston from Fort Henry/— **Back Design:** Plain

Colour: Black

Issue Date: Partially Engraved: _____184_
July 6, Oct. 13, 1842

Imprint: Rawdon, Wright & Hatch

Signatures

Left: mss. illegible **Right:** mss. illegible

Cat. No.	Denom.	Issue Date	G	VG	F	VF	EF	Unc
MU-9	$1 (5s.)	1842	200.	400.	600.	1,000.	2,000.	5,000.
MU-10	$2 (10s)	1842	200.	400.	600.	1,000.	2,000.	5,000.

II. MUNICIPAL COUNCIL OF THE MIDLAND DISTRICT ISSUE 1860-62

Notes of this issue are found with the overprint BANK OF THREE RIVERS in red. Such a bank was actually established in 1841 as Banque des Trois Rivieres but it was unable to complete its organization successfully, and its charter was never used.

MU-11

Face Design: —/oxen pulling hay wagon/—　　**Back Design:** Plain
Colour: Black

MU-12

Face Design: —/woman in ornate V/— **Back Design:** Plain
Colour: Black

Issued Date: Partially Engraved ＿＿＿18＿ Jan. 7, 1860 Jan. 7, 1862　　**Imprint:** Rawdon, Wright, Hatch & Edson, New York

Signatures

Left: mss. I. White or mss. D. Fox　　**Right:** mss. T. Proudfoot mss. D. Thomas

Overprint

$1 (5s.): BANK OF THREE RIVERS in red and ONE vertically at left in green.

£5: BANK OF THREE RIVERS in red and FIVE vertically at left in green.

Cat. No.	Denom.	Issue Date	G	VG	F	VF	EF	Unc
MU-11	$1 (5s.)	1860-62	100.	200.	300.	525.	1,050.	2,500.
MU-12	£5	1860-62	100.	200.	300.	525.	1,050.	2,500.
MU-12a	£5	1860-62 o/p	100.	200.	300.	525.	1,050.	2,500.
MU-12b	£5	18＿ *	100.	200.	300.	525.	1,050.	2,500.

*Remainder note

London

PHOTO NOT AVAILABLE

Face Design: Unknown   **Back Design:** Unknown
Colour: Unknown

Issue Date	**Imprint**	**Signatures**
Unknown	Unknown	Unknown

Cat. No.	Denom.	Issue Date	G	VG	F	VF	EF	Unc
MU-13	5s. ($1)	184–						
MU-14	10s. ($2)	184–						
MU-15	£1 ($4)	184–			ALL VERY RARE			
MU-16	£1.5 ($5)	184–			Estimate: $500. to $1,000.			
MU-17	£2.10 ($10)	184–						

Montreal
Post Office

These notes were probably issued to supply small change during the suspension of specie payments in 1837-38. They were redeemable in current Montreal bank notes when presented in sums of 5 shillings cy. ($1) or more.

MU-18

6d. (12 sous)

Face Design: —/U.S. dime reverse/—   **Back Design:** Plain
Colour: Black

Issue Date	**Imprint**	**Signatures**
Partially Engraved	Unknown	Unknown
_____ July 1837		

Cat. No.	Denom.	Issue Date	G	VG	F	VF	EF	Unc
MU-18	6d. (12 sous)	1837		ALL VERY RARE Estimtate: $500. to $1,000.				

North Vancouver

Wage Payment Certificates

These notes were produced by letterpress. On the backs are listed various business firms in North Vancouver where the notes would presumably be honoured.

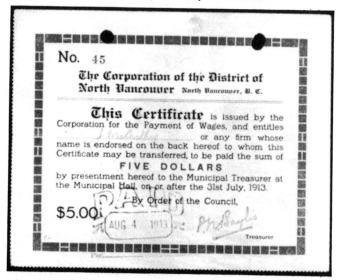

MU-20

Face Design: Wording only
Colour: Black with red border and denomination

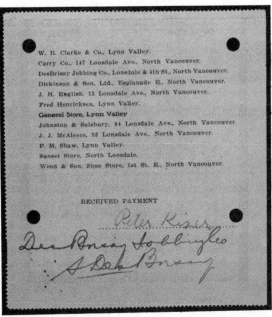

MU-20

Back Design: List of North Vancouver businesses
Colour: Black

Issue Date	Imprint	Signatures
July 31, 1913	None	Stamped: P.L. Bayliss

Cat. No.	Denom.	Issue Date	G	VG	F	VF	EF	Unc
MU-19	$1	1913	25.	55.	85.	150.	300.	750.
MU-20	$5	1913	25.	55.	85.	150.	300.	750.
MU-21	$10	1913	NONE KNOWN TO HAVE SURVIVED					

Peterborough

DISTRICT OF COLBORNE

These crudely produced notes were issued under the authority of the building committee superintending the construction of a court house and jail for the "intended District of Colborne". They were repayable with interest twelve months after date. It is not certain whether these notes ever actually circulated.

MU-22

Face Design: Standing Indian/stag/ seated Justice figure
Colour: Black

Back Design: Plain

Issue Date
Engraved:_____18_

Imprint
None

Signatures
Unknown

Prices are for unsigned, undated remainder notes.

Cat. No.	Denom.	Issue Date	G	VG	F	VF	EF	Unc
MU-22	5s.($1)	18_	75.	150.	230.	400.	800.	2,000.

Portsmouth

PROVINCE OF CANADA

PHOTO NOT AVAILABLE

Face Design: Unknown
Colour: Black

Back Design: Unknown

Issue Date
Unknown

Imprint
Unknown

Signatures
Unknown

Cat. No.	Denom.	Issue Date	G	VG	F	VF	EF	Unc
MU-23	$1	1862	ALL VERY RARE Estimate: $1,000.to $4,000.					

Quebec City

CUSTOM HOUSE

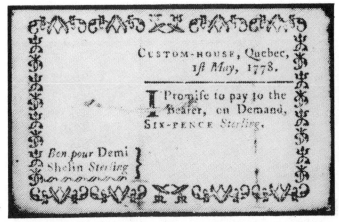

MU-24

Face Design: Wording only
Colour: Black

Back Design: Plain

Issue Date
Engraved: May 1, 1778

Imprint
Unknown

Signatures
Unknown

Cat. No.	Denom.	Issue Date	G	VG	F	VF	EF	Unc
MU-24	6d. (stg.)	1778	ALL VERY RARE Estimate: $1,000. to $4,000.					

City of Saint John

I. FIRST ISSUE

Notes of this issue measure only approximaly 1 3/4" x 3".

MU-25

PHOTO NOT AVAILABLE

MU-26

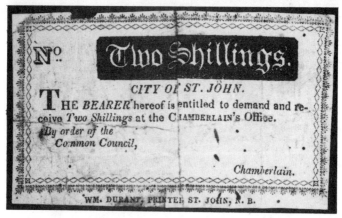

MU-27

Face Design: Wording only   **Back Design:** Plain
Colour: Black

Issue Date: Undated or Engraved: **Imprint:** Wm. Durant, Printer,
March, 1821   St. John N.B.

Signatures
Left: Thomas A, Sancton   **Right:** C.J. Peters

Cat. No.	Denom.	Issue Date	G	VG	F	VF	EF	Unc
MU-25	6d.	1821						
MU-26	1s.3d.	1821			ALL RARE			
MU-27	2s.	(1821)			Estimate: $500. to $2,000.			

58

II. SECOND ISSUE

This 1836 issue is unusual in that the denomination is not engraved on the notes, but is added in manuscript form in the space provided. Many of the surviving notes are remainders, in some cases partially completed. The lathework border reads "City of St. John/Province of/New Brunswick/North America".

MU-28, 29

Face Design: Wording only
Colour: Black

Back Design: Plain

Issue Date: mss. May 26, 1836

Imprint: None

Signatures

Left: mss. various

Right: mss. various

Cat. No.	Denom.	Issue Date	G	VG	F	VF	EF	Unc
MU-28	2s.	1836			ALL RARE			
MU-29	4s.	1836			Estimate: $500. to $2,000.			

III. THIRD ISSUE 1837

Notes of this issue return to the normal printed denomination. The border consists of arcs and rays. Surviving notes which present a crude lithographed appearance are probably contemporary counterfeits.

MU-30

Face Design: Wording only   **Back Design:** Plain
Colour: Black

MU-31

PHOTO NOT AVAILABLE

Face Design: Wording only   **Back Design:** Plain
Colour: Black

Issue Date: mss. June 10, 1837   **Imprint:** None

Signatures
Left: mss. various   **Right:** mss various

Cat. No.	Denom.	Issue Date	G	VG	F	VF	EF	Unc
MU-30	2s.	1837			ALL RARE			
MU-31	4s.	1837			Estimate: $500. to $2,000.			

City of Toronto

UPPER CANADA

The City of Toronto issued Corporation Notes, payable in one year with interest, to pay for public works projects. The notes were repaid with taxation revenue. The first issue, in 1837, was prompted by the refusal of the chartered and private banks to lend money to the city. New issues followed annually, and notes of the previous year were withdrawn and cancelled. In 1848 it was decided that better means of financing existed and the gradual termination of the issue was planned. The last Corporation Notes were issued in 1852.

I. FRACTIONAL ISSUE OF 1837

No notes of this first issue are known to have survived. Denomination, designs, imprint unknown.

II. BURTON, GURLEY & EDMONDS PRINTINGS 1837-ca. 1839

MU-32

Face Design: Crest/Royal Crest/ Indian
Colour: Black

Back Design: Plain

MU-33

Face Design: Crest/cherubs and tablet/woman with spear
Colour: Black

Back Design: Plain

Issue Date: Partially Engraved:
_____1837
Dec. 26, 1837

Partially Engraved:
_____183_
Aug. 20, 1838
(one or two)

Imprint: Burton, Gurley & Edmonds, New York

Signatures

Left: mss. various

Right: mss. A.T. McCord

Cat. No.	Denom.	Issue Date	G	VG	F	VF	EF	Unc
MU-32	$1	1837-1839	250.	500.	750.	1,300.	2,600.	6,500.
MU-33	$2	1837-1839	250.	500.	750.	1,300.	2,600.	6,500.

III. J. ELLIS PRINTING ca. 1840-1847

Around 1840 it was decided to have the Corporation notes printed locally. The designs present a somewhat crude appearance. The illustration below is of a counterfeit $1 (5s.) note.

MU-34

Face Design: Crest/Royal Crest/   **Back Design:** Plain
Indian
Colour: Black

MU-35

Face Design: Crest/woman, bales   **Back Design:** Plain
and ship/standing
woman
Colour: Black

Issue Date: Engraved: _____184_   **Imprint:** J. Ellis Engraver,
Various dates.   Toronto

Signatures

Left: mss. various   **Right:** A.T. McCord

Cat. No.	Denom.	Issue Date	G	VG	F	VF	EF	Unc
MU-34	$1	1841-1847	250.	500.	750.	1,300.	2,600.	6,500.
MU-35	$2	1841-1847	250.	500.	750.	1,300.	2,600.	6,500.

IV. J. ELLIS PRINTING 1848-1852

MU-36

Face Design: Crest/sailing ships/—   **Back Design:** Plain
      Colour: Black

MU-37

Face Design: Crest/seated woman   **Back Design:** Plain
              with plaque/—
      Colour: Black

MU-38

Face Design: Crest/city dockside   **Back Design:** Plain
              scene/—
      Colour: Black

Issue Date: Partially Engraved: **Imprint:** Jno. Ellis & Co. Bank
          _____184_   Note Engravers, 8 King
          Partially Engraved: St. West, Toronto
          _____185_
          Various dates.

Left: mss. various   Right: mss. A.T. McCord

Cat. No.	Denom.	Issue Date	G	VG	F	VF	EF	Unc
MU-36	$1 (5s.)	1848-52	250.	500.	750.	1,300.	2,600.	6,500.
MU-37	$2 (10s.)	1848-52	250.	500.	750.	1,300.	2,600.	6,500.
MU-38	$4 (£1)	1848-52	250.	500.	750.	1,300.	2,600.	6,500.

Warning: Contemporary counterfeits probably outnumber genuine Corporation Notes. The counterfeits are usually badly faded and, in many cases, the imprint is omitted.

PROVINCE OF CANADA

The Province of Canada was formed by the Act of Union of 1841, which united the former colonies of Upper Canada (Ontario) and Lower Canada (Quebec) under a single government. The seat of government was alternatively located in Kingston, Montreal, Toronto and Quebec, until Queen Victoria selected Ottawa to be the permanent capital. The Province was constantly searching for sources from which money could be borrowed to finance such public works as canal construction. Often the credit of the colony was exhausted and a government note issue was eyed as a means of raising an interest-free loan. The banks naturally united to resist this intrusion into what had been their exclusive preserve, until Edwin King, President of the Bank of Montreal and the "Napoleon of Canadian banking" brought his corporation into a brief partnership with the government. The Province of Canada was as unsatisfactory politically as it was financially, and it passed into history with Confederation in 1867.

Provincial Debentures 1848-1850's

In 1848 the government of the Province of Canada, of which Francis Hincks was a member, had to raise funds to meet financial obligations contracted by the previous administration. Unable to borrow either from the financial houses of Great Britain or from the banks at home, the government with Hincks' guidance issued debentures bearing 6% interest. The debentures had the appearance of regular bank notes; they were of small, convenient denominations like bank notes, and they were transferable and reissuable. Although they were only payable in specie one year from the date of issue, they were accepted at any time in payment of accounts due the government.

These were effectively the first Province of Canada notes and although they circulated but briefly, the success of the issue paved the way for future experiments in government-issued currency. Only face proofs are known to have survived. We list them here although specific numbers are not assigned to them.

$1 (5s.)

Face Design: —/seated allegorical female with farm implements, high-way and train in background/—

Colour: Unknown

Back Design: Unknown

Colour: Unknown

$2 (10s.)

Face Design: —/two seated allegorical women with cornucopia and spear/—
Back Design: Unknown

     Colour: Unknown   **Colour:** Unknown

$10 (£2.10)

Face Design: —/seated Britannia and Coat of Arms of the Province of Canada/—
Back Design: Unknown

     Colour: Unknown   **Colour:** Unknown

$20 (£5)

Face Design: —/Royal Crest/—   **Back Design:** Unknown
     Colour: Unknown   **Colour:** Unknown

Issue Date	**Imprint**	**Signatures**
Paritally Engraved: _____185_	Rawdon, Wright & Hatch	None

66

Denom.	Date	Unc
$1 (5s.)	185–	Face Proof $1,500.
$2 (10s.)	185–	Face Proof $1,500.
$10 (£2.10)	185–	Face Proof $1,500.
$20 (£5)	185–	Face Proof $1,500.

I. OVERPRINTED BANK OF MONTREAL NOTE ISSUE

In 1866 the Provincial Note Act was passed as a means to providing the government with funds, all other attempts to raise a loan at reasonable interest having failed. Under its terms, any chartered bank which agreed to surrender its own note issuing privileges could arrange with the government to be an issuing agent for the Provincial notes. Only the Bank of Montreal found the various inducements sufficiently attractive to participate in the plan.

Since the new Province of Canada notes had not yet been prepared in sufficient quantities, stocks of unissued Bank of Montreal notes were overprinted as a temporary measure. Denominations of $4, $5, $10, $20, $50 and $100 of various dates of issue from 1849 to 1862 were overprinted. The overprint, in green or blue, reads "PROVINCIAL NOTE/LEGAL TENDER" horizontally and "PAYABLE IN MONTREAL" or "PAYABLE IN TORONTO" and "FOR THE RECEIVER GENERAL" vertically. The notes were initialled by one of seven persons authorized by the receiver general and signed by one of the officers of the bank.

These notes entered circulation from September to December 1866, when enough of the new Province of Canada notes were on hand to replace them. The overprinted "Legal Tenders" were then rapidly withdrawn. Three whole notes and some fragments produced during the process of cancelling others are known. For further details on the Bank of Montreal Issues please see The Charlton Standard Catalogue of Canadian Bank Notes, Second Edition.

Quantities of Bank of Monteal Notes Overprinted

Denomination	Payable at Montreal	Payable at Toronto
$4	119,000	36,000
$5	68,000	49,000
$10	77,500	41,000
$20	2,500	500
$50	2,500	1,100
$100	2,500	1,200

See Bank of Montreal Issues 505-20 to 505-32 in the Charlton Standard Catalogue of Canadian Bank Notes for information on designs, colours, issue dates, signatures and imprints.

Cat. No.	Denom.	Issue Date	G	VG	F	VF	EF	Unc
PC-1a to PC-1f	$4-$100	1849-62	ALL VERY RARE Estimate: $2,000. to $10,000.					

Issue of 1866

The new notes issued in the name of the Province of Canada and dated at Ottawa entered circulation in January 1867, just a few months before Confederation, when the Province of Canada would disappear as a political entity. The notes however continued to be issued for several years and were the first issued by the Government of the new Dominion of Canada.

Most of the plates were prepared by the American Bank Note Company in New York, but the government had arranged for a new Ottawa firm, the British American Bank Note Company, to do all of the printing. The latter company also engraved the plates for the higher denominations. The notes were printed in denominations of $1, $2, $5, $10, $20, $50, $100 and $500. The $1, $2, and $5 were each printed from 4/on plates with check letters A, B, C and D. The $10 and $20 notes were printed from a mixed plate, arranged 10.10.10.20 with check letters A, B, C, A. The $50 and $100 were each printed from 2/on plates with check letters A and B while the $500 note was printed from a 1/on plate with check letter A. The $100 notes were never issued because the Bank of Montreal, still acting as the government's issuing agent, never asked for them despite reminders that quantities of the notes were available.

The notes were domiciled; that is they were made redeemable in specie (gold) at specific branches of the Receiver General's Office. Originally such branches were set up in Montreal and Toronto. The notes were domiciled by having the location printed vertically in green using separate engraved plates up to the $20. Montreal notes have blue sheet numbers and Toronto notes have red sheet numbers.

All denominations were printed with the engraved signature of the Deputy Receiver General, T. D. Harington. The notes were countersigned at the left by Bank of Montreal personnel, in space designated "Countersigned for Provincial Agents". Plate numbers are present on most of the notes up to $20 and absent on the higher denominations.

All denominations are marked "Canada Bank Note Printing Tint" on the faces. This refers to the green tint used on all the Province of Canada notes. (Distinctive colours for each denomination were not a feature of Canadian government notes until after the printing contracts were taken from the British American Bank Note Co. in 1897). This patented green ink was considered proof against photographic counterfeiting, and was at the time a major development in bank note security.

Summary of Technical Details for 1886 Issues

Cat. No.	Denom.	Variety	Serial Numbers	Quantity Printed
PC-2a	$1	Montreal	000001-187500/A,B,C,D	750,000 (est.)
PC-2b	$1	Toronto	00001-22000	
			47001-62500/A,B,C,D	150,000 (est.)
PC-2c	$1	Toronto, o/p St. John	22001-47000/A,B,C,D	100,000
PC-3a	$2	Montreal	000001-187500/A,B,C,D	750,000 (est.)
PC-3b	$2	Toronto	00001-24000	
			36501-62500/A,B,C,D	200,000 (est.)
PC-3c	$2	Toronto, o/p St. John	24001-36500/A,B,C,D	50,000
PC-4a	$5	Montreal	000001-093750/A,B,C,D	375,000 (est.)
PC-4b	$5	Toronto	00001-17000	
			30751-31250/A,B,C,D	70,000
PC-4c	$5	Toronto, o/p St. John	17001-30750/A,B,C,D	55,000
PC-4d	$5	Halifax	00001-25000/A,B,C,D	100,000
PC-5a	$10	Montreal	000001-045000/A,B,C	135,000 (est.)
PC-5b	$10	Toronto	00001-12000/A,B,C	36,000
PC-5c	$10	Toronto, o/p St. John	12001-16000/A,B,C	12,000
PC-6a	$20	Montreal	000001-045000/A	45,000 (est.)
PC-6b	$20	Toronto	00001-12000/A	12,000 (est.)
PC-6c	$20	Toronto, o/p St. John	12001-16000/A	4,000
PC-7a	$50	Montreal	0001-4000/A,B	8,000 (est.)
PC-7b	$50	Toronto	0001-2000/A,B	4,000 (est.)
PC-7c	$50	Toronto, o/p St. John	2001-4000/A,B	4,000
PC-8a	$100	Montreal	0001-1250/A,B	2,500 (est.)
				(none issued)
PC-8b	$100	Toronto	0001-0875/A,B	1,750 (est)
				(none issued)
PC-9a	$500	Montreal	0001-3000/A	3,000 (est.)
PC-9b	$500	Toronto	0001-2000/A	2,000 (est.)

$1 Issue — 1866

PC-2a

Face Design: Samuel de Champlain/Coat of Arms of the Province of Canada with sailor and farmer/Jacques Cartier Riss portrait)
Colour: Black with green tint (See varieties)

PC-2a

Back Design: Lathework, counters and The Province of Canada
Colour: Green

Issue Date: Engraved: October 1st 1866

Imprint:
Face: American Bank Note Co. New York; British American Bank Note Co. Montreal and Ottawa
Back: American Bank Note Co. N.Y

Printer: British American Bank Note Company

Signatures
Left: mss. various

Right: Engr.: T.D. Harington

Overprint
Toronto Notes: "ST, JOHN" in blue
It is possible that some notes were overprinted "ST. JOHN N.B." but this has not been confirmed.

Varieties
Face Design: PAYABLE AT MONTREAL in green vertically flanking central vignette
PAYABLE AT TORONTO in green vertically flanking central vignette

Cat. No.	Denom.	Variety	G	VG	F	VF	EF	Unc
PC-2a	$1	Montreal	200.	400.	700.	1,400.	2,800.	7,000.
PC-2b	$1	Toronto	300.	600.	900.	1,800.	3,600.	9,000.
PC-2c	$1	Toronto, o/p St. John	750.	1,500.	2,250.	4,500.	9,000.	22,500.

$2 Issues — 1866

PC-3a

Face Design: Indian maiden/seated Britannia with two allegorical women and
boys, train and trestle in background/sailor holding flag, lion
Colour: Black with green tint (See varieties)

PC-3a

Back Design: Lathework, counters and Province of Canada
Colour: Green

Issue Date: Engraved: October 1st
1866

Printer: British American Bank
Note Company

Imprint:
Face: American Bank Note
Co. N. Y. and
British American Bank
Note Co. Montreal and
Ottawa
Back: American Bank Note
Co. N.Y

Signatures
Left: mss. various

Right: Engr.: T.D. Harington

Overprint
Toronto Notes: "ST. JOHN" in blue
It is possible that some notes were overprinted "ST. JOHN N.B." but this has not been confirmed.

Varieties
Face Design: PAYABLE AT MONTREAL in green vertically flanking central
vignette
PAYABLE AT TORONTO in green vertically flanking central
vignette

Cat. No.	Denom.	Variety	G	VG	F	VF	EF	Unc
PC-3a	$2	Montreal	400.	700.	1,400.	2,800.	5,600.	14,000.
PC-3b	$2	Toronto	500.	875.	1,750.	3,500.	7,000.	17,500.
PC-3c	$2	Toronto, o/p St. John	1,000.	1,750.	3,500.	7,000.	14,000.	35,000.

$5 Issue — 1866

PC-4a

Face Design: Queen Victoria (Winterhalter portrait)/Coat of Arms of the Province of Canada with Indian Princess and lion/ship under sail
Colour: Black with green tint (See varieties)

PC-4a

Back Design: Lathework, counters and The Province of Canada
Colour: Green

Issue Date: Engraved: Oct. 1, 1866

Imprint: American Bank Note Co. New York and British American Bank Note Co., Montreal and Ottawa

Printer: British American Bank Note Company

Signatures
Left: mss. various

Right: Engr.: T.D. Harington

Overprint
Toronto Notes: "ST. JOHN" in blue
It is possible that some notes were overprinted "ST. JOHN N.B." but this has not been confirmed.

Varieties
Face Design: PAYABLE AT HALIFAX/ONLY vertically flanking central vignette
PAYABLE AT MONTREAL vertically flanking central vignette
PAYABLE AT TORONTO vertically flanking central vignette

Cat. No.	Denom.	Variety	G	VG	F	VF	EF	Unc
PC-4a	$5	Montreal	800.	1,600.	2,800.	5,600.	11,200.	22,500.
PC-4b	$5	Toronto	800.	1,600.	2,800.	5,600.	11,200.	22,500.
PC-4c	$5	Toronto, o/p St. John	1,000.	2,000.	3,500.	7,000.	14,000.	35,000.
PC-4d	$5	Halifax	900.	1,800.	3,150.	6,300.	12,600.	31,500.

72

$10 Issue — 1866

PC-5b

Face Design: Columbus and sailors/lion, sheaf of wheat, train, anchor and sailing ships/two beavers
Colour: Black with green tint (See varieties)

PC-5b

Back Design: Lathework, counters and Provincial name
Colour: Green

Issue Date: Engraved: Oct. 1, 1866
Printer: British American Bank Note Company

Imprint:
Face: American Bank Note Co. N.Y. and British American Bank Note Co. Montreal and Ottawa
Back: American Bank Note Co. New York

Signatures
Left: mss. various
Right: Engr.: T.D. Harington

Overprint
Toronto Notes: "ST. JOHN" in blue
It is possible that some notes were overprinted "ST. JOHN N.B." but this has not been confirmed.

Varieties
Face Design: PAYABLE AT MONTREAL in green vertically flanking central vignette
PAYABLE AT TORONTO in green vertically flanking central vignette

Cat. No.	Denom.	Variety	G	VG	F	VF	EF	Unc
PC-5a	$10	Montreal	2,000.	4,000.	7,000.	14,000.	28,000.	7,000.
PC-5b	$10	Toronto			FACE PROOF $3,500.			
PC-5c	$10	Toronto, o/p St. John			No notes known to exist.			

Note: No Toronto or Overprinted St. John issued notes are known. Only three Montreal issued notes are known to exist.

$20 Issue — 1866

PC-6a

Face Design: Princess of Wales/four beavers building a dam/Prince Albert
Colour: Black with green tint
See varieties

PC-6a

Back Design: Lathework, counters and Province of Canada
Colour: Green

Issue Date: Engraved: October 1st 1866

Printer: British American Bank Note Company

Signatures
Left: mss. various

Imprint:
Face: American Bank Note Co. New York and British American Bank Note Co. Montreal & Ottawa
Back: American Bank Note Co. N.Y
Right: Engr.: T.D. Harington

Overprint
Toronto Notes: "ST. JOHN" in blue
It is possible that some notes were overprinted "ST. JOHN N.B." but this has not been confirmed.

Varieties
Face Design: PAYABLE AT MONTREAL in green vertically flanking central vignette
PAYABLE AT TORONTO in green vertically flanking central vignette

Cat. No.	Denom.	Variety	G	VG	F	VF	EF	Unc
PC-6a	$20	Montreal	3,000.	6,000.	10,500.	–	–	–
PC-6b	$20	Toronto			FACE PROOF 3,500.			
PC-6c	$20	Toronto, o/p St. John			No notes known to exist.			

Note: No Toronto or Overprinted St. John issued notes are known. Only one Montreal issued note is known.

$50 Issue — 1866

PC-7a

Face Design: —/Mercury holding map of British North America, harbour, ships, train/—
Colour: Black with green tint
(See Varieties)

PC-7b

Back Design: Lathework, counters and Province of Canada.
Colour: Green

Issue Date: Engraved: October 1st 1866

Imprint:
Face: British American Bank Note Co.
Back: British American Bank Note Co. Montreal & Ottawa

Printer: British American Bank Note Company

Signatures
Left: mss. various
Right: Engr.: T.D. Harington

Overprint
Toronto Notes: "ST. JOHN" in blue
It is possible that some notes were overprinted "ST. JOHN N.B." but this has not been confirmed.

Varieties
Face Design: PAYABLE AT MONTREAL horizontally flanking central vignette
PAYABLE AT TORONTO horizontally flanking central vignette

Cat. No.	Denom.	Variety	G	VG	F	VF	EF	Unc
PC-7a	$50	Montreal			FACE PROOF 4,500.			
PC-7b	$50	Toronto			FACE PROOF 4,500.			
PC-7c	$50	Toronto, o/p St. John			No issued notes known to exist.			

$100 Issue — 1866

FACE PHOTO NOT AVAILABLE

PC-8a

Face Design: —/Queen Victoria (Chalon portrait)/—
Colour: Black with green tint (See varieties)

PC-8a

Back Design: Lathework, counters and Province of Canada
Colour: Green

Issue Date: Engraved: October 1st 1866
Printer: British American Bank Note Company

Imprint: British American Bank Note Company

Signatures
Left: None

Right: Engr.: T.D. Harington

Varieties
Face Design: PAYABLE AT MONTREAL horizontally flanking central vignette
PAYABLE AT TORONTO horizontally flanking central vignette

Cat. No.	Denom.	Variety	G	VG	F	VF	EF	Unc
PC-8a	$100	Montreal					FACE PROOF	4,500.
PC-8b	$100	Toronto					FACE PROOF	4,500.

$500 Issue — 1866

PC-9a

Face Design: —/allegorical female and Coat of Arms of the Province of Canada with lion, wheat, bridge and Parliament Building in background/—
Colour: Black with green tint
(See varieties)

PC-9a

Back Design: Lathework, counters and Province of Canada.
Colour: Green

Issue Date: Engraved: October 1st 1866

Printer: British American Bank Note Company

Imprint:
Face: British American Bank Note Co. Montreal & Ottawa
Back: British American Bank Note Co. Montreal & Ottawa

Signatures
Left: None   **Right:** Engr.: T.D. Harington

Varieties
Face Tint: PAYABLE AT MONTREAL horizontally flanking central vignette
PAYABLE AT TORONTO horizontally flanking central vignette

Cat. No.	Denom.	Variety	G	VG	F	VF	EF	Unc
PC-9a	$500	Montreal					FACE PROOF	4,500.
PC-9b	$500	Toronto					FACE PROOF	4,500.

Provincial Notes Issued by the Dominion of Canada

Since Confederation took place only nine months after the Province of Canada notes began to enter circulation, large stockpiles were still on hand in the vaults of the Deputy Receiver General and the Bank of Montreal. It was decided to continue issuing these Provincial notes under the authority of the Dominion of Canada, so that they effectively became the first issue of Dominion notes. This decision was given legal sanction by an act of May 1868 which virtually repeated the Provincial Note Act of 1866, with the term "Dominion" being substituted for "Provincial".

To avoid confusion, and since those notes issued under Provincial and Dominion authority are not completely separable, all will be listed here as Province of Canada issues, consistent with the name on the notes themselves.

With the addition of the Provinces of New Brunswick and Nova Scotia to the federal union, provision had to be made to supply these provinces with government notes. Notes destined for issue in New Brunswick were overprinted "ST. JOHN" in large blue letters across the faces, and were issued through newly established Bank of Montreal branches in the province. These notes have red sheet numbers since Toronto notes were used for overprinting.

Providing notes for Nova Scotia presented a special problem. The currency of Nova Scotia was not assimilated to that of the rest of Canada until 1871. The province was very attached to sterling, and rated the pound sterling at $5.00 Nova Scotia currency, while it rated only $4.86 2/3 in Canada currency. Only $5 Province of Canada notes were sent for issue in Nova Scotia. These were not overprinted Toronto or Montreal notes, but a special printing expressly for use there with the legend "PAYABLE IN HALIFAX/ONLY" vertically in green. These had to be kept within Nova Scotia because they were worth only $4.86 2/3 in the rest of the country. Sheet numbers were black for this special issue. These notes and any others payable in Nova Scotia currency had to be withdrawn after July 1, 1871, when that province was put on a uniform currency basis with the rest of Canada.

The government gradually terminated its relationship with the Bank of Montreal over 1870-1871. Assistant Receiver General offices were set up in the provincial capitals to take over the government note issue and redemption functions which the Bank of Montreal had handled since 1866. The last few Province of Canada notes to be issued had come from the Receiver General's vault and had never been in the possession of the Bank of Montreal. These notes were signed by Bank of Montreal personnel prior to issue. After 1871 the Provincial notes were withdrawn and replaced by Dominion notes. Some stocks of notes from the Receiver General's vault remained unissued and were destroyed.

DOMINION OF CANADA

Issues of 1870

THE 1870 25c FRACTIONAL NOTE

At the time of the American Civil War, U.S. silver coin became depreciated by 5% relative to gold. The situation caused American silver, mostly of the 25-cent and 50-cent denominations, to pour into Canada where it was still received at full face value. Banks and post offices would not accept these coins, so retailers sold them at a discount to brokers, who in turn derived their livelihoods by selling the depreciated silver back to manufacturers and buyers of grain and cattle. Thus the cycle repeated and the "American silver nuisance" resulted in hardship to farmers, merchants and factory workers who had no choice but to accept their losses. The government also suffered, because the $1 and $2 Province of Canada notes, issued by the Dominion government after Confederation, were being crowded out of circulation.

Sir Francis Hincks, minister of Finance in 1870, devised a three-pronged attack on the problem. The government would buy up the American silver at a discount progressing from 5% to 6% and export it, and then peg its legal value at an artificially low 80c on the dollar to ensure against its return to the country. To take its place, the first silver coins for the Dominion of Canada were ordered from the Royal Mint in London. Finally, as a temporary measure, 25 cent fractional notes were to be printed and issued to provide change while the new coinage was being prepared.

The banks were opposed to the introduction of the paper "shinplasters", but the fact that they were redeemable in gold when presented in quantity went a long way toward making the fractional notes acceptable.

Hincks' manoeuvres were eminently successful. Enough American silver was repatriated to New York to saturate the markets there, and the remainder was shipped to England as bullion. There was one unexpected outcome, however, far from being a temporary issue as planned, the fractional notes became popular with the public, and persisted in circulation for the next sixty-five years.

Many attribute the expression "shinplaster" to the use of fractional U.S. notes by soldiers of the Revolutionary War period to prevent their boots from chafing. The term was first used in Canada with reference to the merchants' scrip which appeared in abundance in 1837-38. Subsequently it came to be applied to 25-cent Dominion of Canada notes from the time of their first appearance in 1870.

DETAILS OF THE PRINTING

The 25-cent fractionals were printed in sheets of ten (two across and five down), with no sheet numbers, no check letters and no plate numbers. Eight face plates, fourteen tints and ten back plates were prepared, all in 1870. From these were printed three series of notes. The A series (letter A under the 1870 at the left), consisting of 2,000,000 notes with a total value of $500,000, was issued in 1870. Once the new Dominion silver coinage of 1870 arrived, the need for fractional notes diminished greatly. The B series, also consisting of 2,000,000 notes or $500,000, was printed by 1871 and issued slowly over the period 1871 to 1897, as needed. The plain or no letter series was printed in the 1890's from the old plates, which were modified by the removal of the series letter. Traces of the former series letter can be found on many of these notes. Only about 300,000 of these notes, or $75,000, were issued, but they remain the most readily available to collectors, having been issued most recently.

Summary of Technical Details

Cat.No.	Denom.	Date	Series	Serial Numbers	Quantity Printed
DC-1a	25c	1870	A	None	2,000,000
DC-1b	25c	1870	B	None	2,000,000
DC-1c	25c	1870	Plain	None	300,000 (est.)

DC-1c

Face Design: —/Britannia/—
Colour: Black with green tint

Back Design: Lathework and "redeemable on presentation at Montreal, Toronto or St. John."
Colour: Green

Issue Date: Engraved: March 1st 1870

Imprint: British American Bank Note Co. Montreal & Ottawa

Signatures
Left: Engr.: W. Dickinson

Right: Engr.: T.D. Harington

Varieties

This issue carried no serial numbers but had series letters which are immediately below the 1870 of the left hand date on the face of the note.

Series Letter A

Series letter B

Plain (no series letter)

Cat. No.	Denom.	Series	G	VG	F	VF	EF	AU	Unc
DC-1a	25c	A	25.	60.	125.	250.	625.	950.	1,600.
DC-1b	25c	B	5.	15.	40.	100.	250.	375.	625.
DC-1c	25c	Plain	3.	7.	20.	45.	115.	175.	300.

THE 1870 $1 AND $2 NOTES

Apart from the fractionals, these are the only other denominations of this issue to enter ordinary circulation in quantity. Unlike the fractionals, which were redeemable in any of Montreal, Toronto or St. John, the $1 and $2 notes were specifically designated on their backs as being payable in Montreal, Toronto, St. John, Halifax or Victoria. The back design was different for each city. The only difference on the faces occurred in the sheet numbers, which were partially colour-coded as follows:

Montreal	blue	6-digit numbers	Halifax	black	5-digit numbers
Toronto	red	6-digit numbers	Victoria	blue	5-digit numbers
St. John	black	5-digit numbers			

Special backs were not engraved for the notes issued by the Assistant Receiver General at Winnipeg. However, at least some of the notes were stamped MANITOBA vertically in black ink across the right end of the faces of Toronto and Montreal notes. The purpose behind rubber stamping these notes appears to have been to establish their migration pattern, rather than to indicate that they were payable at Winnipeg. Two $1 and $2 notes with the MANITOBA stamp are known to have survived.

The engraved signatures are those of William Dickinson, Inspector General, on the space "For Minister of Finance" and T. D. Harington, Deputy Receiver General, in the space "For Receiver General". A third manuscript signature occurs vertically across the left end of the face, except for the Halifax notes, where it is sometimes found across the right end. These countersignatures were applied either in Ottawa or at the offices of the various Assistant Receivers General.

Both denominations are dated July 1st, 1870, although they were not released for circulation until well into 1871. The provincial notes were thereafter eventually withdrawn.

The $1 note has a fine portrait of Jacques Cartier at the left and an allegorical vignette called "Canada" at the centre. The Cartier portrait is taken from a painting by F. Riss (circa 1840-1866). It hangs in the Hotel de Ville of St. Malo, the port from which Cartier sailed on his memorable voyage to the New World in 1534. Riss is said to have taken as his model a pen drawing in the Bibliotheque Nationale, Paris, but this drawing has never been located. Of all the denominations of the first Dominion note issue, the $1 alone lacks any reference to the authorizing legislation (31 Vict. cap. 36).

The $2 has at the left end a portrait of General Wolfe and at the right end a portrait of General Montcalm, both of whom were killed on the Plains of Abraham in 1759. The centre vignette, called "Civilization" or "Nor'West" shows an Indian seated on a bluff, watching a train passing below.

The $1 Toronto notes were counterfeited extensively. The counterfeits can be identified by the presence of a course black dot for Cartier's eye.

The $1 and $2 notes were printed from 4/on plates, with check letter A, B, C and D. The $1 notes bear plate numbers at the right of the check letters, while the $2 notes have them at the right of or below the check letters, or have none at all.

Summary of Technical Details

Cat.No.	Denom.	Date	Variety	Series	Serial Numbers	Quantity Printed
DC-2a	$1	1870	Montreal	Plain	000001-650000/A,B,C,D	2,600,000 (est.)
DC-2b	$1	1870	Toronto	Plain	000001-587500/A,B,C,D	2,250,000 (est.)
DC-2c	$1	1870	St. John	Plain	00001-75000/A.B.C,D	300,000 (est.)
DC-2d	$1	1870	Halifax	Plain	00001-110000/A,B,C,D	440,000 +
DC-2e	$1	1870	Victoria	Plain	00001-12500/A,B,C,D	50,000 (est.)
DC-3a	$2	1870	Montreal	Plain	000001-191000/A,B,C,D	764,000 (est.)
DC-3b	$2	1870	Toronto	Plain	000001-182000/A,B,C,D	728,000 (est.)
DC-3c	$2	1870	St. John	Plain	00001-37500/A,B,C,D	150,000 (est.)
DC-3d	$2	1870	Halifax	Plain	00001-100000/A,B,C,D	400,000 (est.)
DC-3e	$2	1870	Victoria	Plain	00001-06200/A,B,C,D	24,000 (est.)

$1 Issue — 1870

DC-2a

Face Design: Jacques Cartier (Riss portrait)/allegorical female pointing
to Canada's location on a globe "Canada"/—
Colour: Black with green tint

DC-2a

Back Design: Lathework, counters and "Payable at (city name)"
Colour: Green
Issue Date: July 1, 1870

Imprint: British American Bank
Note Co. Montreal &
Ottawa on the face and
back

Signatures
Left: Engr.: W. Dickinson   **Right:** Engr.: T.D. Harington
Additional: mss. various (vertically), usually at the left end

Varieties

DC-2b

DC-2c   **Photo Not Available**

DC-2d

DC-2e

Domicile: Printed across the back is the location of the Assistant Receiver General's office at which the particular note was payable;
PAYABLE AT MONTREAL
PAYABLE AT MONTREAL, Stamped "Manitoba"in black, vertically at right.
PAYABLE AT TORONTO
PAYABLE AT TORONTO, Stamped "Manitoba"in black, vertically at right.
PAYABLE AT ST. JOHN
PAYABLE AT HALIFAX
PAYABLE AT VICTORIA (2 known)

 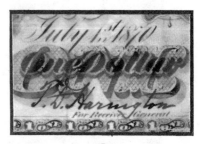

Small   Date   Large Date

Engraved Date: The Montreal and Toronto notes have a small and large engraved date.

Cat. No.	Denom.	Variety	G	VG	F	VF	EF	AU	Unc
DC-2a	$1	Montreal, SD	80.	175.	350.	700.	1,575.	2,400.	4,000.
DC-2ai	$1	Montreal, LD	80.	175.	350.	700.	1,575.	2,400.	4,000.
DC-2aii	$1	Montreal, Manitoba	2,000.	5,000.	8,750.	–	–	–	–
DC-2b	$1	Toronto, SD	80.	175.	350.	700.	1,575.	2,400.	4,000.
DC-2bi	$1	Toronto, LD	80.	175.	350.	700.	1,575.	2,400.	4,000.
DC-2bii	$1	Toronto, Manitoba	2,000.	5,000.	8,750.	–	–	–	–
DC-2c	$1	St. John	500.	1,200.	2,400.	4,800.	9,500.	–	–
DC-2d	$1	Halifax	400.	1,000.	2,000.	4,000.	8.000.	–	–
DC-2e	$1	Victoria	2,000.	5,000.	8,750.	–	–	–	–

$2 Issue — 1870

DC-3a

Face Design: General Wolfe/Indian chief on bluff watching train below,
"Nor'West"/General Montcalm
Colour: Black with green tint

DC-3a

Back Design: Lathework, counters and "Payable at (City name)"
Colour: Green

Issue Date: Engraved: July 1st 1870   **Imprint:** British American Bank
Note Co. Montreal &
Ottawa on the face and
back

Signatures
Left: Engr.: W. Dickinson   **Right:** Engr.: T.D. Harington
Additional: mss. various (vertically), usually at the left end

Varieties

DC-3b

DC-3ai

DC-3c

DC-3d

DC-3e

Domicile: Printed across the back is the location of the Assistant Receiver General's office at which the particular note was payable;
PAYABLE AT MONTREAL
PAYABLE AT MONTREAL, Stamped "Manitoba"in black, vertically at right.
PAYABLE AT TORONTO
PAYABLE AT TORONTO, Stamped "Manitoba"in black, vertically at right.
PAYABLE AT ST. JOHN
PAYABLE AT HALIFAX
PAYABLE AT VICTORIA

Cat. No.	Denom.	Variety	G	VG	F	VF	EF	AU	Unc
DC-3a	$2	Montreal	500.	1,500.	2,250.	4,000.	8,000.	12,000.	–
DC-3ai	$2	Montreal, Manitoba	2,500.	5,000.	–	–	–	–	–
DC-3b	$2	Toronto	600.	1,800.	2,700.	5,500.	11,000.	16,500	–
DC-3bi	$2	Toronto, Manitoba	2,500.	5,000.	–	–	–	–	–
DC-3c	$2	St. John	1,000.	3,000.	4,500.	9,000.	18,000.	–	–
DC-3d	$2	Halifax	900.	2,700.	4,000.	8,000.	16,000.	–	–
DC-3e	$2	Victoria			No notes known to exist				

Issues of 1871-1872

The first and only Dominion notes of $50 and $100 denominations are dated March 1, 1872, and the first $500 and $1000 Dominion notes are dated July 1, 1871. These denominations were primarily held by the chartered banks to secure their note circulation, but they were also legal tender for ordinary transactions. The $50 and $100 notes were too large to find much use among the public and were too small to be convenient for the banks. So small was the demand for them that no other Dominion note issues inluded these denominations.

Each of the higher denomination notes bears a single vignette at its centre. The "Mercury" vignette on the $50 had formerly been used on the Province of Canada $50. The newly built Parliament Buildings appear on the $100. The Chalon portrait of Queen Victoria is found on the $500 while the $1000 uses the reclining woman and coat of arms vignette previously used on the Province of Canada $500.

Like the $1 and $2 of 1870, all of these notes were domiciled, with the city where the notes could be redeemed indicated on their backs. The $50 and $100 were payable in Montreal or Toronto only. The $500 and $1000 were payable originally in Montreal, Toronto, St. John and Halifax. Later, special backs were engraved for Victoria, Winnipeg and Charlottetown. Notes domiciled at the latter two cities were issued in 1891 and 1892 respectively.

The $50 and $100 notes were each printed from 2/on plates, with check letters A and B. The $500 and $1000 were both printed from a single 2/on plate. The $500 was given check letter A, while the $1000 had none. No plate numbers seem to have been used, and it is likely that only one set of plates was used in each case. The sheet numbers had only four digits. No signatures were engraved on the plates; all issued notes were signed and countersigned by hand. Proof notes, of course, have no signatures.

These notes are now extremely rare. One Montreal and one Toronto $50, as well as another partial Montreal $50, survive. One fragment of each of $100, $500 and $1000 notes, all payable in Montreal, survive. All are in the Bank of Canada Currency collection. The last $100 Dominion note was turned in to the Department of Finance in 1918.

Summary of Technical Details

Cat.No.	Denom.	Date	Variety	Series	Serial Numbers		Quantity Printed
DC-4a	$50	1872	Montreal	Plain	0001-...	/A,B	Unknown
DC-4b	$50	1872	Toronto	Plain	0001-...	/A,B	...
DC-5a	$100	1872	Montreal	Plain	0001-...	/A,B	...
DC-5b	$100	1872	Toronto	Plain	0001-...	/A,B	...
DC-6a	$500	1871	Montreal	Plain	0001-...	/A	...
DC-6b	$500	1871	Toronto	Plain	0001-...	/A	...
DC-6c	$500	1871	St. John	Plain	0001-...	/A	...
DC-6d	$500	1871	Halifax	Plain	0001-...	/A	...
DC-6e	$500	1871	Victoria	Plain	0001-0420/A		420
DC-6f	$500	1871	Winnipeg	Plain	0001-0150/A		150
DC-6g	$500	1871	Charlottetown	Plain	0001-...	/A	...
DC-7a	$1000	1871	Montreal	Plain	0001-...	/A	...
DC-7b	$1000	1871	Toronto	Plain	0001-...	/A	...
DC-7c	$1000	1871	St. John	Plain	0001-...	/A	...
DC-7d	$1000	1871	Halifax	Plain	0001-...	/A	...
DC-7e	$1000	1871	Victoria	Plain	0001-0420/A		420
DC-7f	$1000	1871	Winnipeg	Plain	0001-0150/A		150
DC-7g	$1000	1871	Charlottetown	Plain	0001-...	/A	...

$50 Issue — 1872

DC-4

Face Design: —/Mercury holding a map of British North America/—
Colour: Black with green tint

DC-4b

Back Design: Lathework, counters and "Payable at (City name)"
Colour: Green

Issue Date: Engraved: Mar. 1. 1872

Imprint: British American Bank
Note Company

Signatures
Left: mss. various

Right: mss. various

Varieties
Printed across the back is the location of the Assistant Receiver General's office at which the
particular note was payable:
PAYABLE AT MONTREAL; PAYABLE AT TORONTO

Cat. No.	Denom.	Variety	G	VG	F	VF	EF	Unc
DC-4	$50	No City	Plain				FACE PROOF	1,000.
DC-4a	$50	Montreal	Plain				BACK PROOF	300.
DC-4b	$50	Toronto	Plain				BACK PROOF	300.

$100 Issue — 1872

DC-5a

Face Design: —/Parliament Buildings/—
Colour: Black with green tint

BACK PHOTO NOT AVAILABLE

DC-5a

Back Design: Lathework, counters and city name
Colour: Green

Issue Date: Engraved: 1st March 1872

Imprint: British American Bank Note Co. Montreal & Ottawa

Signatures

Left: mss. various

Right: mss. various

Varieties

Printed across the back is the location of the Assistant Receiver General's office at which the particular note was payable.

PAYABLE AT MONTREAL; PAYABLE AT TORONTO

Cat. No.	Denom.	Variety	G	VG	F	VF	EF	Unc
DC-5	$100	No City	Plain				FACE PROOF	3,500.
DC-5a	$100	Montreal	Plain				BACK PROOF	1,000.
DC-5b	$100	Toronto	Plain				BACK PROOF	1,000.

$500 Issue — 1871

DC-6b

Face Design: —/Queen Victoria (Chalon portrait)/—
Colour: Black with green tint

DC-6b

Back Design: Lathework, counters and "Payable at (City name)"
Colour: Green

Issue Date: July 1st 1871

Imprint: British American Bank Note Co. Montreal and Ottawa

Signatures
Left: mss. various

Right: mss. various

Varieties
Printed across the back is the location of the Assistant Receiver General's office at which the particular note was payable.

PAYABLE AT MONTREAL
PAYABLE AT TORONTO
PAYABLE AT ST. JOHN
PAYABLE AT HALIFAX

PAYABLE AT VICTORIA
PAYABLE AT WINNIPEG
PAYABLE AT CHARLOTTETOWN

Cat. No.	Denom.	Variety	Series	G	VG	F	VF	EF	Unc
DC-6	$500	No City	Plain					FACE PROOF	3,500.
DC-6a	$500	Montreal	Plain					BACK PROOF	1,000.
DC-6b	$500	Toronto	Plain		ONLY			BACK PROOF	1,000.
DC-6c	$500	St. John	Plain		PROOFS			BACK PROOF	1,000.
DC-6d	$500	Halifax	Plain		KNOWN			BACK PROOF	1,000.
DC-6e	$500	Victoria	Plain					BACK PROOF	1,000.
DC-6f	$500	Winnipeg	Plain					BACK PROOF	1,000.
DC-6g	$500	Charlottetown	Plain					BACK PROOF	1,000.

$1000 Issue — 1871

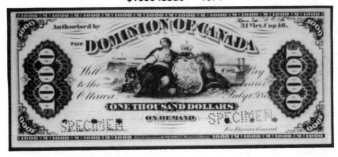

DC-7

Face Design: —/Coat of Arms of the Dominion flanked by lion and reclining woman/—
Colour: Black with green tint.

BACK PHOTO NOT AVAILABLE

Back Design: Lathework, counters and "Payable at (City name)"
Colour: Green

Issue Date: Engraved: July 1st 1871

Imprint: British American Bank Note Co. Montreal & Ottawa

Signatures
Left: mss. various

Right: mss. various

Varieties

Printed across the back is the location of the Assistant Receiver General's office at which the particular note was payable.

PAYABLE AT MONTREAL
PAYABLE AT TORONTO
PAYABLE AT ST. JOHN
PAYABLE AT HALIFAX

PAYABLE AT VICTORIA
PAYABLE AT WINNIPEG
PAYABLE AT CHARLOTTETOWN

Cat. No.	Denom.	Variety	Series	G	VG	F	VF	EF	Unc
DC-7	$1,000	No City	Plain					FACE PROOF	3,500.
DC-7a	$1,000	Montreal	Plain					BACK PROOF	1,000.
DC-7b	$1,000	Toronto	Plain		ONLY			BACK PROOF	1,000.
DC-7c	$1,000	St. John	Plain		PROOFS			BACK PROOF	1,000.
DC-7d	$1,000	Halifax	Plain		KNOWN			BACK PROOF	1,000.
DC-7e	$1,000	Victoria	Plain					BACK PROOF	1,000.
DC-7f	$1,000	Winnipeg	Plain					BACK PROOF	1,000.
DC-7g	$1,000	Charlottetown	Plain					BACK PROOF	1,000.

Issues of 1878

A plausible reason for preparing a new issue of $1 and $2 notes so soon after the introduction of the first Dominion note was the counterfeiting of the Toronto $1's. If the purpose of the 1878 issue was to improve security, it failed badly. The ones were "raised" to resemble $4 notes and the two's were extensively counterfeited.

With this issue began the practice of placing the portraits of the Governor General and his wife on the faces of the Dominion notes. The Countess of Dufferin appears on the $1 note and the Earl of Dufferin, the eloquent and popular Governor General of Canada from 1872 to 1878, appears on the $2 denomination. The back designs of both denominations indicate the location of the Assistant Receiver General's office at which the note was payable, and portrays the Great Seal of Canada.

The 1878 $1 and $2 notes were domiciled at the same four cities as the 1870 issue, but this time bore the name of the city on the face, just above the countersignature, as well as on the back. Again the sheet numbers were colour coded, this time with:

Montreal	blue
Toronto	red
St. John	black
Halifax	green

The St. John and Halifax $2's had five-digit numbers; all others had six. The domiciling of notes ended with this issue.

The only engraved signature is that of T. D. Harington, the Deputy Receiver General, who had retired before any of the notes had actually entered circulation. The left signature space, "For Minister of Finance", was left blank for the manuscript countersignature so that it could be applied horizontally. About 1882-83 the Finance Department hired women to countersign the notes, a task previously the preserve of men.

The new notes were not released until stocks of the old notes were used up, and did not enter circulation until August 1879. The initial $1 notes had a scalloped frame with a large "scallop" in each corner. The Finance Department was soon disturbed to find that some of the Toronto $1 notes were being "raised" to resemble $4's by skillfully changing the large 1 counters to 4's with pen and ink, and altering the ONE's. The British American Bank Note Co. responded by making a number of design alterations, most of them intended to make raising more difficult. The scalloped border was replaced by a lettered border repeating the inscription "1 ONE DOLLAR", and "1" counters replaced the scallops in the corners. The word ONE was added across the large "1" counters at either end.

Both Montreal and Toronto $2 notes were extensively counterfeited, leading to the retirement of the Dufferin $2 note after 1887, while the lettered border $1's were issued for another decade. Many of the counterfiet notes are still in existence, outnumbering the genuine notes, and the collector should beware of them. The counterfeits usually contain at least one "1" digit in the sheet number, and it has a sloping top. Genuine notes of this issue have flat-topped "1's".

Flat-Topped 1
(Genuine)

Curved-Topped 1
(Counterfeit)

As in 1870 the $1 and $2 "Dufferin" notes of 1878 were printed from 4/on plates, with check letters A, B, C and D. It was during this issue that the series letter was introduced in these denominations. After the printing of 1,000,000 sheets, the sheet numbering was started over at 000001 and a new series begun. Normally, and unlike the example of the fractionals, the first series was "plain", that is, had no series letter. The first sheets of $1 notes were of the scalloped border variety, and when the lettered border $1 was introduced, numbering resumed where it had left off with the scalloped border notes. When enough sheets were printed to reach number 1000000, series A began, starting at 000001 and going up to 1000000 again, then series B began, and so on.

Care must be taken to avoid confusion of the series letter with the check letter, particularly since the check letter was moved when the lettered border was adopted.

SCALLOPED BORDER $1 1878:
The check letter is the large solid black letter A, B, C, or D to the immediate left of the sheet number. There is no series letter ("plain").

LETTER BORDER $1 1878:
The check letter is the gothic letter below the sheet number. The series letter (A, B, C or none) the white faced letter to the left of the sheet number.

The face plate number, if it is present at all, is a tiny black number located as follows:

SCALLOPED BORDER $1's and all $2's: left of the left-hand check letter.

LETTERED BORDER $1's: above the D of DOMINION or above the last A of CANADA.

About 1889 the British American Bank Note Company moved from Montreal to Ottawa. This change was reflected in the imprint on the backs of the notes. The imprint on the face was not changed.

$1 Issue — 1878 Scalloped Border

Summary of Technical Details

Cat.No.	Denom.	Date	Variety	Series	Serial Numbers	Quantity Printed
DC-8a	$1	1878	Scalloped, Montreal	Plain	000001-200000/A,B,C,D	800,000
DC-8b	$1	1878	Scalloped, Toronto	Plain	000001-200000/A,B,C,D	800,000
DC-8c	$1	1878	Scalloped, St. John	Plain	000001-050000/A,B,C,D	200,000
DC-8d	$1	1878	Scalloped, Halifax	Plain	000001-050000/A,B,C,D	200,000

$1 Issue — 1878 Scalloped Border

Scalloped Border: No "1's" in the smaller corner counters and no overprint "ONE" on the large "1's" in the main right and left counters.

DC-8a

Face Design: —/Countess of Dufferin/—
Colour: Black with green tint

DC-8a

Back Design: —/Great Seal of Canada/—
Colour: Green

Issue Date: Engraved: June 1st 1878

Imprint

Face: British American Bank
Note Co. Montreal

Back: British American Bank
Note Co. Montreal
orBritish American Bank
Note Co. Ottawa

Signatures

Left: mss. various

Right: Engr.: T.D. Harington

Varieties

The various Assistant Receiver General office locations at which the note was payable appear around the Great Seal.

PAYABLE AT MONTREAL   PAYABLE AT HALIFAX
PAYABLE AT TORONTO   PAYABLE AT ST. JOHN

DC-8b

DC-8c

DC-8d

Cat. No.	Denom.	Variety	Series	G	VG	F	VF	EF	AU	Unc
DC-8a	$1	Montreal	Plain	100.	250.	375.	650.	1,300.	1,950.	3,250.
DC-8b	$1	Toronto	Plain	100.	250.	375.	650.	1,300.	1,950.	3,250.
DC-8c	$1	St. John	Plain	500.	1,000.	1,500.	2,600.	5,200.	7,800.	–
DC-8d	$1	Halifax	Plain	500.	1,000.	1,500.	2,600.	5,200.	7,800.	–

$1 Issue — 1878 Lettered Border

Summary of Technical Details

Cat.No.	Denom.	Date	Variety	Series	Serial Numbers	Quantity Printed
DC-8e	$1	1878	Lettered, Montreal	Plain	200001-1000000/A,B,C,D	3,200,000
DC-8e-i	$1	1878	Lettered, Montreal	A	000001-1000000/A,B,C,D	4,000,000
DC-8e-ii	$1	1878	Lettered, Montreal	B	000001-1000000/A,B,C,D	4,000,000
DC-8e-iii	$1	1878	Lettered, Montreal	C	000001-800000/A,B,C,D	3,200,000 (est.)
DC-8f	$1	1878	Lettered, Toronto	Plain	200001-1000000/A,B,C,D	3,200,000
DC-8f-i	$1	1878	Lettered, Toronto	A	000001-1000000/A,B,C,D	4,000,000
DC-8g	$1	1878	Lettered, St. John	Plain	050001-075000/A,B,C,D	100,000
DC-8h	$1	1878	Lettered, Halifax	Plain	050001-100000/A,B,C,D	200,000

"1" and "ONE DOLLAR" are alternately repeated in the border. "1's" are placed in the corner counters and the large "1's" in the main right and left counters are overprinted with "ONE".

DC-8e

Face Design: —/Countess of Dufferin/—
Colour: Black with green tint

DC-8h

Back Design: —/Great Seal of Canada/—
Colour: Green

Issue Date: Engraved: 1st June 1878
Imprint
Face: British American Bank
Note Co. Montreal

Back: British American Bank
Note Co. Montreal
orBritish American Bank
Note Co. Ottawa

Signatures

Left: mss. various   **Right:** Engr.: T.D. Harington

Varieties

The various Assistant Receiver General office locations at which the note was payable appear around the Great Seal.

PAYABLE AT MONTREAL   PAYABLE AT HALIFAX
PAYABLE AT TORONTO   PAYABLE AT ST. JOHN

Cat. No.	Denom.	Variety	Series	G	VG	F	VF	EF	AU	Unc
DC-8e	$1	Montreal	Plain	25.	50.	75.	125.	250.	400.	650.
DC-8e-i	$1	Montreal	A	25.	50.	75.	150.	250.	400.	650.
DC-8e-ii	$1	Montreal	B	25.	50.	75.	125.	250.	400.	650.
DC-8e-iii	$1	Montreal	C	25.	50.	75.	125.	250.	400.	650.
DC-8f	$1	Toronto	Plain	25.	50.	75.	125.	250.	400.	650.
DC-8f-i	$1	Toronto	A	25.	50.	75.	125.	250.	400.	650.
DC-8g	$1	St. John	Plain	500.	1,000.	1,500.	2,600.	5,200.	7,800.	–
DC-8h	$1	Halifax	Plain	500.	1,000.	1,500.	2,600.	5,200.	7,800.	–

$2 Issue — 1878

Summary of Technical Details

Cat.No.	Denom.	Date	Variety	Series	Serial Numbers	Quantity Printed
DC-9a	$2	1878	Montreal	Plain	000001-350000/A,B,C,D	1,400,000 (est.)
DC-9b	$2	1878	Toronto	Plain	000001-230000/A,B,C,D	920,000 (est.)
DC-9c	$2	1878	St. John	Plain	00001-12500/A,B,C,D	50,000
DC-9d	$2	1878	Halifax	Plain	00001-32500/A,B,C,D	130,000

$2 Issue — 1878

DC-9c

Face Design: —/Earl of Dufferin/—
Colour: Black with green tint

DC-9b

Back Design: —/Great Seal of Canada
Colour: Green

DC-9c

Genuine   **Counterfeit**

Issue Date: Engraved: June 1st 1878
Imprint
Face: British American Bank
Note Co. Montreal

Back: British American Bank
Note Co. Montreal
orBritish American Bank
Note Co. Ottawa

Signatures
Left: mss. various   **Right:** Engr.: T.D. Harington

Varieties

The various Assistant Receiver General office locations at which the note was payable appear around the Great Seal.

PAYABLE AT MONTREAL   PAYABLE AT HALIFAX
PAYABLE AT TORONTO   PAYABLE AT ST. JOHN

Note: Beware of counterfiet notes of this issue. The counterfiets will have poor engraving of the portrait and lathework.

Cat. No.	Denom.	Variety	Series	G	VG	F	VF	EF	AU	Unc
DC-9a	$2	Montreal	Plain	250.	500.	750.	1,500.	3,000.	4,000.	7,000.
DC-9b	$2	Toronto	Plain	275.	550.	800.	1,600.	3,200.	4,800.	8,000.
DC-9c	$2	St. John	Plain	500.	1,000.	1,500.	3,000.	6,000.	9,000.	15,000.
DC-9d	$2	Halifax	Plain	375.	750.	1,125.	2,250.	4,500.	6,750.	11,000.

$4 Issue of 1882

In 1880 the Dominion Government assumed the right to issue $4 notes, restricting the banks whose charters were coming up for renewal to the issue of denominations of $5 and its multiples. The first $4 Dominion notes entered circulation in October 1882.

The central vignette portrays the Marquis of Lorne, Governor General from 1878 to 1883. The Marquis married H.R.H. Princess Louis, the second daughter of Queen Victoria, but the match was not a happy one. He later succeeded his father as Duke of Argyll.

The green tint at the left consists of an ornate numeral 4 flanked by two cherubs and partially obscures a view of Montreal's Victoria Bridge. At the right, the Great Seal of Canada, found on the backs of previous issues, occurs in orange ink.

The $4 note is dated at Ottawa, and represents the end of the policy of the Finance Department to make its notes payable at a specific Assistant Receiver General's office.

To provide additional security, the $4 notes were printed on watermarked paper, the only instance of such paper being used for Canadian government notes. The watermark consists of the words DOMINION OF CANADA on two intersecting bands, with a maple leaf, shamrock, rose and thistle at the intersection. The paper tended to tear along the watermark and was also too thin to hold up satisfactorily in circulation.

The engraved signature of J. M. Courtney, Deputy Minister of Finance from 1878 to 1906, is found at the right, while the Finance Department's clerks applied their manuscript signatures at the left, in the space marked "countersigned".

The notes of this issue never formed a very large component of the Dominion notes in circulation. The final stocks of these notes entered circulation in April, 1900.

The 1882 $4 notes were printed in sheets of four with check letters A, B, C and D. Four face plates, numbered 1, 2, 3 and 4, were laid down in March and April of 1882. The plate numbers are found just below the right-hand check letter. Additional plates were used for the tint, the seal and the back.

Summary of Technical Details for $4 Issue

Cat.No.	Denom.	Date	Variety	Series	Serial Numbers	Quantity Printed
DC-10	$4	1882	Plain		000001-300000/A,B,C,D	1,200,000

$4 Issue — 1882

DC-10

Face Design: Ornate 4, Cherubs, Victoria Bridge/Marquis of Lorne/Great Seal
of Canada*
Colour: Black with green tint

* The Great Seal of Canada was originally orange in colour; however the ink is unstable and
will vary in colour from orange to brown as a result of oxidization.

DC-10

Back Design: Lathework, counters and "Dominion of Canada"
Colour: Green

Issue Date: Engraved: May 1st, 1882
Note Co.

Imprint: British American Bank
Montreal on
face and back

Signatures

Left: mms. various

Right: Engr.: J.M. Courtney

Cat. No.	Denom.	Series	G	VG	F	VF	EF	UF	Unc
DC-10	$4	Plain	250.	500.	750.	1,500.	3,000.	4,500.	7,500.

Issue of 1887

A new issue of $2 notes was released in the fall of 1887 to replace the 1878 "Dufferin" notes, probably because of extensive counterfeiting of the latter.

Portraits of the Marquis and Marchioness of Lansdowne appear on the face of the note. The Marquis served as Governor General of Canada from 1883 to 1888. The back is unusual in that it is printed in two colours, black and green. Two printing runs, involving different plates, were needed to print such backs, making them more difficult to counterfeit. The back vignette, entitled "Quebec", shows Jacques Cartier and his men aboard ship.

Following the precendent established by the Lorne $4 notes, the Landowne $2 notes were not domiciled, but rather were dated at Ottawa for general use.

The notes bear the engraved signature of J. M. Courtney in the right-hand space designated "FOR MINISTER OF FINANCE" while the left-hand space contains the manuscript signature of any of various women employed by the Finance Department for the purpose of countersigning the notes.

The first, or "plain", series entered circulation between 1887 and 1896, when it was completed. The second series, designated "A", was then begun. The "A" series was discontinued late in 1897.

The notes were printed in sheets of four, with check letters A, B, C and D. The check letters are located above the portraits. The series letter, if there is one, is the solid black "A" below each sheet number. The face plate number occurs just above the right-hand check letter.

Summary of Technical Details

Cat.No.	Denom.	Date	Series	Serial Numbers	Quantity Printed
DC-11	$2	1887	Plain	000001-1000000/A,B,C,D	4,000,000
DC-11-i	$2	1887	A	000001-150000/A,B,C,D	600,000 (est.)

$2 Issue — 1887

DC-11

Face Design: Marchioness of Lansdowne/—/Marquis of Lansdowne
Colour: Black with green tint

DC-11

Back Design: Lathework, counters and Jacques Cartier's arrival at Quebec/—
Colour: Black and green

Issue Date: Engraved: July 2nd, 1887

Imprint: British American Bank Note Co. Montreal on face and back

Signatures

Left: mss. various

Right: Engr.: J.M. Courtney

Cat. No.	Denom.	Series	G	VG	F	VF	EF	AU	Unc
DC-11	$2	Plain	100.	225.	450.	900.	1,800.	2,700.	4,500.
DC-11-i	$2	A	150.	300.	600.	1,200.	2,400.	3,600.	6,000.

Issues of 1897 and 1898

In 1897 the Canadian Government terminated its relationship with the British American Bank Note Co., and directed its security printing orders to the American Bank Note Co., New York. The American firm then established a branch plant in Ottawa, primarily to handle the government printing. This necessitated that new designs be prepared for all denominations of Dominion notes, although stocks on hand of the higher denominations were sufficient to last for several years.

The $1 notes dated 1897 portray the Countess and Earl of Aberdeen, and a logging scene in the centre. The Earl was Governor General from 1893 to 1898. Lady Aberdeen founded the Victoria Order of Nurses in commemmoration of Queen Victoria's Diamond Jubilee, and was founding president of the National Council of Women. The backs depict the Centre Block of the Parliament Buildings, as seen from Wellington Street.

The $2 notes portray Edward, Prince of Wales, at the left. Following the death of Queen Victoria in 1901, he reigned as King Edward VII until his own death in 1910. A fishing scene vignette occupies the centre of the note. On the back of the note is a grain harvesting scene.

Both denominations of the first American Bank Note Co. issue of Dominion notes underwent modifications soon after the first deliveries were made to the Finance Department in August 1897. Both denominations were originally printed with green faces, so it was decided to change the $1 tint colour to light brown to better distinguish it from the $2. The issue dating was changed to March 31, 1898, although the first notes were not received by the Finance Department until September of that year. The lathework border was replaced by a lettered one. The large "1" counters on the backs of the 1897 $1 issue tended to show through the paper, disfiguring the portraits on the faces, so they were replaced by smaller counters.

The 1897 $1 notes have no series letter. The 1898 notes begin with series A, even though the plain series had not been completed, and continue to series S. This marks a change in procedure, henceforth the Dominion note issues begin with the "A" series rather than a plain series.

Two varieties are found on the backs of the $1 1898 issue. Those received by the Finance Department between September 1898 and June 1903 have the "ONE" counters curved inward, and later notes have the "ONE" counters curved outward. The last sheet printed with the "ONE's" inward was number 800000 in series D. A new series was not immediately begun, but series D resumed with sheet number 800001, with the "ONE's" outward. The last delivery of 1898 $1 notes was made to the Finance Department in May 1911.

The first printings of the 1897 $2 note have a red-brown back. After June 1898 all $2 notes were printed with a dark brown back. The red-brown backs were not discovered by collectors until recent years, and are very scarce. Only sheets numbered 000001 to 175000 in the "plain" series have red-brown backs. Dark brown backs began with sheet number 175001 and continued to the end of the plain series and through series A to I. The last known delivery of the 1897 $2 notes was made to the Finance Department in June 1914, after which several years records were destroyed.

The notes were printed in sheets of four with check letter A, B, C and D. The original engraved signature on the right was that of J. M. Courtney, Deputy Minister of Finance until 1906 when he retired and was succeeded by T. C. Boville. The signature changeover was not made immediately, and the delivery of Boville notes did not begin until August 1907 in the case of the $1 denomination and January 1908 for the $2's. The countersignatures at the right were applied by the women retained by the Finance Department for the exclusive purpose of signing notes.

The use of planchetted paper as an additional security device began during this issue of Dominion notes. The first $1 notes of the 1898 issue to contain these tiny embedded discs of coloured paper began with sheet number 046501 in the "C" series (delivered October 1901). Planchetted paper was also used for the 1897 dated $2 notes from sheet number 182501 in series "C", onward.

The check letters are located on either side of the central vignettes on each denomination. The series letter, if there is one, is found below each sheet number on the $1 notes and below the central vignette on the $2 notes. The plate numbers were not printed on the notes, with the exception of some of the last Boville $2 1897 notes.

Checklist of Prefix Letters for 1897-1898 $1 Issues

Cat.No.	Denom.	Variety	Signature	Series Letters
DC-12	$1		Courtney	Plain
DC-13a	$1	ONE's Inward	Courtney	A B C D
DC-13b	$1	ONE's Outward	Courtney	D E F G H I J K
DC-13c	$1	ONE's Outward	Boville	L M N O P Q R S

Summary of Technical Details

Cat.No.	Denom.	Date	Variety	Series	Serial Numbers	Quantity Printed
DC-12	$1	1897		Plain	000001-600000/A,B,C,D	2,400,000
DC-13a	$1	1898	Courtney, ONE's	A	000001-1000000/A,B,C,D	4,000,000
			(Inward)	B	000001-1000000/A,B,C,D	4,000,000
				C	000001-1000000/A,B,C,D	4,000,000
				D	000001-800000/A,B,C,D	3,200,000
DC-13b	$1	1898	Courtney, ONE's	D	800001-1000000/A,B,C,D	800,000
			(Outward)	E	000001-1000000/A,B,C,D	4,000,000
				F	000001-1000000/A,B,C,D	4,000,000
				G	000001-1000000/A,B,C,D	4,000,000
				H	000001-1000000/A,B,C,D	4,000,000
				I	000001-1000000/A,B,C,D	4,000,000
				J	000001-1000000/A,B,C,D	4,000,000
				K	000001-1000000/A,B,C,D	4,000,000
DC-13c	$1	1898	Boville, ONE's	L	000001-1000000/A,B,C,D	4,000,000
			(Outward)	M	000001-1000000/A,B,C,D	4,000,000
				N	000001-1000000/A,B,C,D	4,000,000
				O	000001-1000000/A,B,C,D	4,000,000
				P	000001-1000000/A,B,C,D	4,000,000
				Q	000001-1000000/A,B,C,D	4,000,000
				R	000001-1000000/A,B,C,D	4,000,000
				S	000001-670000/A,B,C,D	2,680,000

$1 Issue — 1897

DC-12

Face Design: Countess of Aberdeen/logging on a Canadian river/
Earl of Aberdeen
Colour: Black with green tint

DC-12

Back Design: Lathework, counters and Parliament Building, view of the centre
block from the front gate/—
Colour: Green

Issue Date: Engr.: July 2nd, 1897

Imprint: American Bank Note
Co. Ottawa

Signatures

Left: mss. various

Right: Engr.: J.M. Courtney

Cat. No.	Denom.	Variety	Series	G	VG	F	VF	EF	AU	Unc
DC-12	$1		Plain	100.	200.	400.	800.	1,600.	2,400.	4,000.

$1 Issue — 1898

DC-13a

Face Design: Countess of Aberdeen/logging on a Canadian river/
Earl of Aberdeen
Colour: Black with light brown tint

DC-13a

ONE's curved inward

DC-13b

ONE's curved outward

Back Design: Lathework, counters and Parliament Building, view of the centre block from the front gate/—
Colour: Green

Issue Date: Engr.: March 31st, 1898 **Imprint:** American Bank Note Company Ottawa on face and back

Signatures
Left: mss. various **Right:** Engr.: J.M. Courtney
mss. various T.C. Boville

Varieties

Two different back designs were used for the "ONE" counters at the left and right ends of the note back:

ONE's curved inward

ONE's curved outward

Cat. No.	Denom.	Variety	Series	G	VG	F	VF	EF	AU	Unc
DC-13a	$1	Courtney, ONE's inward	A,B,C,D	25.	50.	100.	200.	400.	600.	1,000.
DC-13b	$1	Courtney, ONE's outward	D,E,F,G, H,I,J,K	15.	30.	60.	125.	250.	375.	625.
DC-13c	$1	Boville, ONE's outward	L,M,N,O, P,Q,R.S	15.	30.	60.	125.	250.	375.	625.

$2 Issue — 1897

Checklist of Prefix Letters for $2 Issues

Cat.No.	Denom.	Variety	Signature	Series Letters
DC-14a	$2	Red-brown back	Courtney	Plain
DC-14b	$2	Dark brown back	Courtney	Plain A B C
DC-14c	$2	Dark brown back	Boville	D E F G H I

Summary of Technical Details

Cat.No.	Denom.	Date	Variety	Series	Serial Numbers	Quantity Printed
DC-14a	$2	1897	Courtney red-brown back	Plain	000001-175000/A,B,C,D	700,000
DC-14b	$2	1897	Courtney dark brown back	Plain	175001-1000000/A,B,C,D	3,300,000
				A	000001-1000000/A,B,C,D	4,000,000
				B	000001-1000000/A,B,C,D	4,000,000
				C	000001-1000000/A,B,C,D	4,000,000
DC-14c	$2	1897	Boville dark brown back	D	000001-1000000/A,B,C,D	4,000,000
				E	000001-1000000/A,B,C,D	4,000,000
				F	000001-1000000/A,B,C,D	4,000,000
				G	000001-1000000/A,B,C,D	4,000,000
				H	000001-1000000/A,B,C,D	4,000,000
				I	000001-242000/A,B,C,D*	968,000 +

*Last recorded delivery. Records of shipments after June 1914 were destroyed.

$2 Issue — 1897

DC-14a

Face Design: Edward, Prince of Wales, six men in a fishing dory/—
Colour: Black with green tint

DC-14c

Back Design: —/Agricultural Industry allegory/—
Colour: See varieties

Issue Date: July 2nd, 1897

Imprint: American Bank Note Co. Ottawa

Signatures

Left: mss. various
mss. various

Right: Engr.: J.M. Courtney
Engr.: T.C. Boville

Varieties

$2: Back Colour: Red-brown; dark brown

Cat. No.	Denom.	Variety	Series	G	VG	F	VF	EF	AU	Unc
DC-14a	$2	Courtney, red-brown back	Plain	500.	1,000.	1,500.	2,600.	5,200.	7,500.	–
DC-14b	$2	Courtney, dark brown back	Plain A,B,C	30.	65.	95.	170.	350.	50.	–
DC-14c	$2	Boville, dark brown back	D,E,F,G, H,I	25.	50.	75.	150.	200.	450.	750.

Issues of 1900 and 1902

In 1900 the American Bank Note Company added the 25-cent and $4 notes to the denominations of Dominion notes it was preparing on behalf of the government. These were only the second issues of each value to be released. Three major varieties are known for each.

25c ISSUE — 1900

The 1900 "shinplasters" portray a seated Britannia figure, with trident and shield. The vignette was engraved by Mr. Goodeve of the American Bank Note Company's engraving department in New York. THe backs, consisting only of lathework and counters, omit any reference to cities where the notes were payable, consistent with the policy of no longer domiciling Dominion notes.

There is only a single engraved signature, that of the Deputy Minister of Finance. Initially the notes were signed by J. M. Courtney, Deputy Minister from 1878 to 1906. T. C. Boville followed, from 1906 to 1920 and J. C. Saunders served as Deputy Minister from 1920 to 1929. The notes signed by Courtney have the word OTTAWA in large black letters to the right of the signature, but it does not appear on notes signed by his successors.

The 25-cent fractional notes were printed in sheets of ten until 1918. From 1918 they were printed in sheets of twenty. There is no check letter or sheet number, consistent with the 1870 issue. There is also no series letter.

The first of the Courtney shinplasters were received by the Finance Department in July 1900. They were printed on paper differing from that used for the contemporary $1 and $2 notes. A strip of coloured planchettes was used as an added security feature.

Plate numbers did not appear on the Courtney notes, but may be found on notes bearing other signatures. The face plate number is located under the 25 counter at the upper left or upper right, and the back plate number is at the lower right. Plate number combinations seen in conjunction with the two signatures are as follows:

Plate Number Combinations for 1900 Issue Fractionals

A. Signed T.C. Boville		B. Signed J.C. Saunders	
Face Plate #'s	Back Plate #'s	Face Plate #'s	Back Plate #'s
None,13, 14, 15, 16	None	29	15, 16
17	None, 12	30	15, 16
18	None, 12	31	17, 18
19	None, 9, 10, 11, 12	31	17, 18
20	None, 9, 10, 11, 12	32	17, 18
21	9, 10, 11, 12		
22	9, 10, 11, 12		
23	9, 10		
24	9, 10		
25	15, 16		
26	15, 16		

Unfortunately, bank note company records for note deliveries covering the period from mid-1914 to late 1921 were destroyed, so the total number of notes printed and issued is not available. However, it is known that between 1900 and mid-1914 3,360,000 of the fractional notes were received. These had either the Courtney or the Boville signature. Another 1,960,000 of the 1900 type arrived at the Finance Department in 1922 and 1923, all presumably with the Saunders signature.

Summary of Technical Details

Cat.No.	Denom.	Date	Variety	Series	Serial Numbers	Quantity Printed
DC-15a	25c	1900	Courtney	None	None	...
DC-15b	25c	1900	Boville	None	None	...
DC-15c	25c	1900	Saunders	None	None	...

25c Issue — 1900

DC-15b

Face Design: —/—/Britannia seated on her shield, sailing ship in background
Colour: Black with light brown tint

DC-15b

Back Design: Lathework and counters
Colour: Green

Issue Date: Engr.: January 2nd, 1900

Imprint: American Bank Note Company, Ottawa on face and back

Signatures

Left: Engr.: J.M. Courtney
Engr.: T.C. Boville
Engr.: J.C. Saunders

Right: None
None
None

Cat. No.	Denom.	Variety	G	VG	F	VF	EF	AU	Unc
DC-15a	25c	Courtney	3.	6.	10.	18.	36.	55.	90.
DC-15b	25c	Boville	2.	4.	6.	12.	25.	45.	75.
DC-15c	25c	Saunders	4.	8.	12.	20.	40.	60.	100.

$4 ISSUE OF 1900 AND 1902

The portraits on the $4 notes of 1900 and 1902 are those of the Countess and Earl of Minto, the latter being Governor General from 1898 to 1904. The central vignette features the Sault Ste. Marie locks, which connect Lake Superior and Lake Huron. Through an error, the United States side of the locks was shown on the 1900 issue instead of the Canadian side. The error was corrected on the 1902 issue. The backs of both issues depict the Parliament Buildings as seen from Nepean Point.

The 1900 $4 notes were delivered to the Finance Department from December 1900 to February 1902, at which time the 1902-dated issue became available. The initial 1902-dated notes have large "4" counters in the upper corners and "FOUR's" in the lower corners, The last notes of this type were delivered in January, 1903.

Thereafter no more $4 notes were printed, probably because the change to the $5 denomination was receiving active consideration, until the summer of 1911. It was then that a sudden, unexpected need for large supplies of paper currency arose. New designs having "FOUR's" in the corners had been ordered by the Finance Department late in 1902, to facilitate sorting. Models were submitted for government approval in 1910, and plates incorporating these changes and other slight changes in the tints were eventually engraved. With the urgent need for notes, they were pressed into service and additional plates engraved. The bank note company worked day and night, with all available presses running, to cope with the rush orders. Between June and September of 1911 the entire production of the final type of $4 notes was delivered to the Finance Department. No more $4 Dominion notes were ever ordered. The denomination which was so important in colonial times, because it was equivalent to one pound Halifax currency, had become obsolete.

Twenty-four face plates were engraved in 1911, and were used together with eight backs and eight tints, whereas eight of each could have been sufficient had production been carried out at a normal pace.

All varieties of the $4 notes of 1900 and 1902 were printed in sheets of four, with check letters A, B, C and D flanking the central vignette. Following the procedure established in 1898, all are designated "Series A", whereas the previous practice had been to begin a new issue with a "plain" (i.e. no letter) series, and begin the "A" series for the second million sheets. First, there was a 1900 Series "A", with sheets numbered from 000001 to 105000, and then there was a 1902 Series "A", in which the sheet numbers started over at 000001. Sheets of this series had the large "4" counters at the top corners up to number 110000, after which "FOUR" counters appeared at the top corners. Plate numbers do not appear on any of the notes.

The 1900 issue, as well as the 1902 notes with the "4" counters on top, bear the engraved signature of J. M. Courtney at the right. The 1902-dated notes (actually printed in 1911) with the "FOUR" counters on top have the engraved signature of T. C. Boville. All received manuscript countersignatures on the left at the Department of Finance prior to issue.

By 1912 the $4 denomination was being withdrawn from circulation and replaced by $5 Dominion notes. Only small quantities of the outstanding $4 notes were turned in after the end of 1915, and by 1950 all but $29,000 worth, of all dates of issue, had been withdrawn, and most of those still outstanding have probably been lost through fire and decay.

Summary of Technical Details

Cat.No.	Denom.	Date	Variety	Series	Serial Numbers	Quantity Printed
DC-16	$4	1900	Courtney, U.S. Locks	A	000001-105000/A,B,C,D	420,000
DC-17a	$4	1902	Courtney, 4's at top	A	000001-110000/A,B,C,D	440,000
DC-17b	$4	1902	Boville, FOUR's at top	A	110001-519000/A,B,C,D	1,636,000

DC-16

Face Design: Countess of Minto/Sault Ste. Marie U.S. locks/Earl of Minto
See Varieties
Colour: Black with green tint

DC-16

Back Design: —/Parliament Buildings and Library, view from the Ottawa River/—
Colour: Green

Issue Date: Engraved: July 2nd, 1900　　**Imprint:** American Bank Note
Company, Ottawa

Signatures
Left: 1900: miss. various　　**Right:** Engr.: J.M. Courtney

Cat. No.	Denom.	Variety	G	VG	F	VF	EF	AU	Unc
DC-16	$4	Courtney	100.	200.	400.	800.	1,600.	2,400.	4,000.

$4 Issue — 1902

The face of the $4 1902 issues used two designs on the upper left and right corner counters; large "4's" at top — large "FOUR's" at top.

DC-17a

Face Design: Countess of Minto/Sault Ste. Marie Canadian locks/ Earl of Minto
Colour: Black with green tint

DC-17a

Back Design: —/Parliament Buildings and Library, view from the Ottawa River/—
Colour: Green

Issue Date: Engraved: Jany 2nd, 1902   **Imprint:** American Bank Note Company, Ottawa

Signatures
Left: 1902: mss. various   **Right:** Engr.: J.M. Courtney

Cat. No.	Denom.	Variety	G	VG	F	VF	EF	AU	Unc
DC-17a	$4	Courtney, 4's on top	85.	175.	350.	700.	1,400.	2,100.	3,500.

DC-17b

Face Design: Countess of Minto/Sault Ste. Marie Canadian locks/Earl of Minto
Colour: Black with green tint

DC-17b

Back Design: —/Parliament Buildings and Library, view from the
Ottawa River/—
Colour: Green

Issue Date: Engraved: Jany. 2nd, 1902

Imprint: American Bank Note Company, Ottawa

Signatures
Left: 1902: mss. various

Right: Engr.: T.C. Boville

Cat. No.	Denom.	Variety	G	VG	F	VF	EF	AU	Unc
DC-17b	$4	Boville, FOUR's on top	75.	150.	225.	400.	800.	1,200.	2,000.

Issues of 1911

$1 ISSUE — 1911

The $1 note issue dated 1911 began to be delivered to the Finance Department in May 1911, superseding the Aberdeen issue. Vignettes of the Earl and Countess of Grey occupy the centre of the notes. Earl Grey was Governor General from 1904 to 1911, a longer term than usual. The Greys were very popular and their period in office was extended at the request of the Canadian government. The backs were unchanged from the previous issue.

The early notes of this issue have a green lathework line along the top edge of the signature panel. On later issues the tint was modified by the removal of this line, and a black lathework line was added to the face plate. The bank note company made this change in its plates in mid-1914.

There was a good deal of experimentation with the series letter during the period of this issue. The first three series printed, series A, B and C, have the series letter engraved on both sides of the portraits just above the signature panel. The check letters are found near the upper corners. For series D, E, F and G, the engraved series letters and the check letters have interchanged positions. This change was made on the plates early in 1912. Thereafter, the series letter, printed by the letterpress method in red ink, follows the sheet number, while the check letters remain flanking the portraits. Series H, J, K and L occur in conjunction with the green lathework border on the signature panel, and series M through Y were only printed with the black lathework border. Series U, V, W, X and Y have the series letter separated from the sheet number by a hyphen. Series letters I, O, Q and Z were not used.

All varieties bear the engraved signatures of T. C. Boville in the area designated FOR MINISTER OF FINANCE, and the manuscript signatures of various employees of the Finance Department in the area designated COUNTERSIGNED. Face plate numbers are found below the second 1 in the top left border, and back plate numbers are found at the lower right corner. The notes were printed sometimes from 4/on, but more frequently from 8/on, plates. In all cases check letters A, B, C and D were used. For 8/on plates, the sheets were arranged

A	A
B	B
C	C
D	D

with different numbers being used for each side of the sheet.

Checklist of Prefix Letters for 1911 $1 Dominion Notes

Cat.No.	Variety	Series Letter
DC-18a	Green line, Series Letter engraved above signature panel.	ABC
DC-18b	Green line, Series Letter engraved near upper corners.	DEFG
DC-18c	Green line, Series Letter follows sheet number, no hyphen	HJKL
DC-18d	Black line, Series Letter follows sheet number, no hyphen	LMNPRST
DC-18d-i	Black line, Series Letter follows sheet number, with hyphen	UVWXY

Summary of Technical Details

Cat.No.	Denom.	Date	Variety	Series	Serial Numbers	Quantity Printed
DC-18a	$1	1911	Green Line, Series Letter Engr. Bottom	A	000001-1000000/A,B,C,D	4,000,000
				B	000001-1000000/A,B,C,D	4,000,000
				C	000001-1000000/A,B,C,D	4,000,000
DC-18b	$1	1911	Green Line, Series Letter Engr. Top	D	000001-1000000/A,B,C,D	4,000,000
				E	000001-1000000/A,B,C,D	4,000,000
				F	000001-1000000/A,B,C,D	4,000,000
				G	000001-1000000/A,B,C,D	4,000,000
DC-18c	$1	1911	Green Line, Series Letter after Sheet No.	H	000001-1000000/A,B,C,D	4,000,000
				J	000001-1000000/A,B,C,D	4,000,000
				K	000001-1000000/A,B,C,D	4,000,000
				L	000001-Unknown/A,B,C,D	Unknown
DC-18d	$1	1911	Black Line, No Hyphen	L	234411-1000000/A,B,C,D	Unknown
				M	000001-1000000/A,B,C,D	4,000,000
				N	000001-1000000/A,B,C,D	4,000,000
				P	000001-1000000/A,B,C,D	4,000,000
				R	000001-1000000/A,B,C,D	4,000,000
				S	000001-1000000/A,B,C,D	4,000,000
				T	000001-1000000/A,B,C,D	4,000,000
DC-18d-i	$1	1911	Black Line, Hyphen	U	000001-1000000/A,B,C,D	4,000,000
				V	000001-1000000/A,B,C,D	4,000,000
				W	000001-1000000/A,B,C,D	4,000,000
				X	000001-1000000/A,B,C,D	4,000,000
				Y	000001-1000000/A,B,C,D	4,000,000

$1 Issue — 1911

DC-18d

Face Design: —/Earl of Grey, Countess of Grey/—
See varieties
Colour: Black with green tint

DC-18b

Back Design: —/Parliament Buildings, view of the centre block from the
front gate/—
Colour: Green

Issue Date: Engraved: Jany. 3rd,
1911

Imprint: American Bank Note
Company, Ottawa

Signature

Left: mss. various

Right: Engr.: T.C. Boville

Varieties

In the face design a line encloses the microlettering and signatures, just below the right and left counters, which was printed in two colours.

Green line   **Black line**

Cat. No.	Denom.	Variety	Series	VG	F	VF	EF	AU	Unc
DC-18a	$1	Green line, Series Letter engraved above signature panel	A,B,C	30.	45.	80.	160.	240.	400.
DC-18b	$1	Green line, Series Letter engraved near upper corners	D,E,F,G	25.	40.	70.	140.	210.	350.
DC-18c	$1	Green line, Series Letter follows sheet No., no hyphen	H,J,K,L	30.	45.	80.	160.	240.	400.
DC-18d	$1	Black line, Series Letter follows sheet No., no hyphen	L,M,N,P, R,S,T	15.	25.	45.	90.	135.	225.
DC-18d-i	$1	Black line, Series Letter follows sheet No., with hyphen	U,V,W, X,Y	25.	40.	70.	140.	210.	350.

$500 and $1000 Issues of 1911

Consultations between the American Bank Note Co. and the Comptroller of Currency had taken place in 1902 concerning a new issue of $50 and $100 Dominion notes. No new issues of these denominations were ever printed however, and the denominations were discontinued. New designs for $500 and $1000 notes had been ordered in February 1911, and by the spring of that year the stocks on hand of the 1871 issue were finally depleted. A 4/on plate was prepared for the $1000 note in August and one for the $500 note in December of 1911. There were no check letters A, B, C or D on the notes, the sheets being cut up and the notes numbered individually and consecutively before delivery to the Finance Department. Red six-digit serial numbers were used. Both denominations have "SERIES A" engraved upon the faces of the notes. They bore no engraved signatures, but were signed by hand at the Finance Department. The final delivery was made in 1924.

The central vignettes on the new $500 and $1000 Dominion notes were current portraits of Queen Mary and King George V respectively. To distinguish the higher denomination notes from the Bank Legals, or "Specials", they were called "Bearer Notes" by government officials, because they were payable to the "bearer".

Summary of Technical Details

Cat.No.	Denom.	Date	Series	Serial Numbers	Quantity Printed
DC-19	$500	1911	A	000001-044000	44,000
DC-20	$1000	1911	A	000001-034000	34,000

H. M. QUEEN MARY.

$500 Issue — 1911

DC-19

Face Design: —/H.M. Queen Mary/—
Colour: Black with green tint

DC-19

Back Design: Lathework, counters and "Dominion of Canada"
Colour: Green

Issue Date: Engraved: Jany. 3rd, 1911

Imprint: American Bank Note Company, Ottawa

Signatures

Left: mss. various

Right: mss. various

Cat. No.	Denom.	G	VG	F	VF	EF	AU	Unc
DC-19	$500	750.	1,000.	1,250.	1,800.	3,100.	4,400.	7,000.
DC-19	$500			SPECIMEN				9,000.

$1000 Issue — 1911

DC-20

Face Design: —/Admiral portrait of King George V/—
Colour: Black with blue tint

DC-20

Back Design: Lathework, counters and "Dominion of Canada"
Colour: Blue

Issue Date: Engraved: Jany. 3rd, 1911

Imprint: American Bank Note Company, Ottawa

Signatures

Left: mss. various

Right: mss. various

Cat. No.	Denom.	G	VG	F	VF	EF	AU	Unc
DC-20	$1000	1,250.	1,500.	1,750.	2,300.	3,600.	4,900.	7,500.
DC-20	$1000			SPECIMEN				1,000.

Issue of 1912

Work began on a $5 Dominion note issue as early as 1906. Some of the designs which were considered included a Nova Scotia mining scene, portraits of the Earl and Countess Grey, and the train vignette which was finally chosen for the issue of 1912. The Coat of Arms and the Great Seal of Canada were both contemplated for the back design but were not used.

The issued note portrays an attractive vignette of a passenger train, the "Maritime Express", travelling through the Wentworth Valley in Nova Scotia. The back consists of lathework and Roman and Arabic numberal counters.

It occurred to officials of the Finance Deparment that hand signing of Dominion notes was not really necessary, and it was decided to acquire special presses for the application of the second signature. This change in procedure was made in 1922, with the first notes of the $5 denomination to be machine-signed arriving in August. The word "COUNTERSIGNED" was removed from over the left signature space and was replaced by the words "COMPTROLLER OF CURRENCY" below the space. When the final signature was applied, a large blue Finance Department seal was added as an additional security device.

The original intention was to have the denominational counter at the right removed, making room for the seal, before machine-signing any notes. However, difficulties were being experienced with the ink used for hand-signing the notes. It did not adhere properly to the paper for some denominations. Accordingly it was decided to begin machine signing before the counters could be removed, creating the transitional "seal over" varieties.

The first series of the 1912 $5 issue had "SERIES A" engraved below the sheet numbers. The sheets were delivered to the Finance Department between June 1912 and January 1916. Despite the number issued, series "A" notes are now very scarce because no hoards have ever turned up.

With the beginning of the "B" series, the black engraved series letter was removed and, for a short time, was printed in red **following** the sheet number. Such notes are likewise very scarce. Soon the "B" series letter moved to **precede** the sheet number. These notes are now perhaps the most readily available variety since substantial hoards, all with check letter C and sheet numbers beginning 4650— and 4717—, have been placed on the market. All of the preceding bear the engraved signature of T. C. Boville and a manuscript countersignature.

A transitional variety follows, with the Finance Department seal applied over the right FIVE counter, and either the signature of T. C. Boville or J. C. Saunders engraved at the right. The left hand signature, printed on the notes at the same time as the seal, is that of G. W. Hyndman. The "seal over FIVE" notes were delivered to the Finance Department between August 1922 and September 1923, with the signature changeover occurring in October 1922.

About September 1923 the right FIVE counter and lathework were removed, and the seal applied in the resulting space. The last of series "B" and all of series "C" were printed with this arrangement. The signature combination on nearly all of these "seal only" notes is Hyndman-Saunders, and the last notes with this signature combination were received in October 1924. No more $5 Dominion notes were printed until October 1931, when a few more were printed, still in series "C", with the McCavour-Saunders signatures.

The McCavour-Saunders note is rare; in fact only a single example has been discovered at the time of writing, and it is in the Bank of Canada currency collection. The series "B", "seal only" note is very scarce. The series "C" Hyndmand-Saunders note is easily obtainable, particularly because of the discovery of a hoard, with check letter D and sheet numbers beginning 1443—.

In 1923 the American Bank Note Company, Ottawa, changed its name to the Canadian Bank Note Company, Limited. Accordingly, the imprints on both faces and backs were altered to reflect this change. The imprint changeover seems to have begun with the "C" series.

The $5 train notes were sometimes printed from 4/on, but usually from 8/on plates. The plate numbers are absent on the earlier varieties, but are found on later varieties just above and left of the last A in CANADA on the face, and at the lower right on the back.

Checklist of Prefix Letter for 1912 $5 Dominion Notes

Cat.No.	Denom.	Variety	Signature	Series Letters
DC-21a	$5	Engraved "SERIES A", no seal	Boville, r.	A
DC-21b	$5	Series Letter "B" follows sheet number; no seal	Boville, r.	B
DC-21c	$5	Series Letter, "B" precedes sheet number; no seal	Boville, r.	B
DC-21d	$5	Seal over FIVE	Hyndman-Boville	B
DC-21e	$5	Seal over FIVE	Hyndman-Saunders	B
DC-21f	$5	Seal only	Hyndman-Saunders	B C
DC-21g	$5	Seal only	McCavour-Saunders	C

Summary of Technical Details

Cat.No.	Denom.	Variety	Series	Serial Numbers	Quantity Printed
DC-21a	$5	Boville, r. (no seal)	A	000001-1000000/A,B,C,D	4,000,000
DC-21b	$5	Boville, r. B after sheet number (no seal)	B	000001-... /A,B,C,D	2,196,000
DC-21c	$5	Boville, r. B before sheet number (no seal)	B	465052- 549000/A,B,C,D	
DC-21d	$5	Hyndman-Boville (seal over FIVE)	B	549001- 663287/A,B,C,D	1,804,000
DC-21e	$5	Hyndman-Saunders (seal over FIVE)	B	... - 714925/A,B,C,D	
DC-21f	$5	Hyndman-Saunders (seal only)	B	... -1000000/A,B,C,D	3,000,000
			C	000001- 750000/A,B,C,D	
DC-21g	$5	McCavour-Saunders (seal only)	C	750001- 754750/A,B,C,D	19,000

$5 Issue — 1912

DC-21f

Face Design: —/passenger train travelling through the Wentworth Valley in Nova Scotia/—
Colour: Black with blue tint

DC-21a

Back Design: Lathework, counters and "Dominion of Canada"
Colour: Blue

Issue Date: Engraved: May 1st 1912

Imprint: American Bank Note Company, Ottawa
Canadian Bank Note Company Limited

Signatures

Left: mss. various
Typed: G. W. Hyndman
Typed: G. W. Hyndman
Types: S. P. McCavour

Right: Engr.: T. C. Boville
Engr.: T. C. Boville
Engr.: J. C. Saunders
Engr.: J. C. Saunders

Varieties

The seal of the Department of Finance is used during the middle of this issue and is over-printed on, or replaces the right FIVE of the right counter.

FIVE at right   **Blue seal over FIVE at right**   **Blue seal only**

Cat. No.	Denom.	Variety	Series	G	VG	F	VF	EF	AU	Unc
DC-21a	$5	No seal, Boville, r.	A	35.	70.	100.	175.	350.	550.	900.
DC-21b	$5	No seal, Boville, r., B after sheet no.	B	17.	35.	50.	90.	180.	270.	450.
DC-21c	$5	No seal, Boville, r., B before sheet no.	B	17.	35.	50.	90.	180.	270.	450.
DC-21d	$5	Hyndman-Boville, seal over FIVE	B	75.	150.	225.	400.	800.	1,200.	2,000.
DC-21e	$5	Hyndman-Saunders, seal over FIVE	B	75.	110.	170.	300.	600.	900.	1,500.
DC-21f	$5	Hyndman-Saunders, seal only	B,C	45.	90.	135.	250.	500.	750.	1,200.
DC-21g	$5	McCavours-Saunders, seal only	C	750.	1,500.	Only one known.				

Issue of 1914

The 1897 "Prince of Wales" issue of $2 Dominion notes was finally replaced in 1914. Portraits of the Duke and Duchess of Connaught appear on the face of the new note and the back portrays the Canadian Coat of Arms surrounded by the provincial shields. The Duke, born Prince Arthur, was the third and favourite son of Queen Victoria. He came to Canada as a member of the Red River expedition of 1870, and Prince Arthur's Landing (later Port Arthur, and now part of Thunder Bay) was named in his honour. He was promoted to Field Marshal of the British Army in 1902, and was Governor General of Canada from 1911 to 1916. The Duke sometimes tended to make pronouncements upon Canadian military policy during World War I, which aroused some controversy. He organized the Canadian Patriotic Fund to assist dependants of servicemen.

The initial printings of the $2 Dominion notes of 1914 have the words "WILL PAY TO THE BEARER ON DEMAND" curved around the large 2 counter at the centre of the note. Two subvarieties of this type exist. The series letter is found immediately after the sheet number, with no hyphen, for series A, B and C. A hyphen separates the sheet number from the series letter for series D, E, F, G, H, J and the low-numbered notes of series K.

In January 1920 the plates were modified so that "WILL PAY TO THE BEARER ON DEMAND" appears in a straight line. At the same time it was decided to put the series letter in front of the sheet number, retaining the hyphen. The signature engraved on the lower right side of these and the preceding notes is that of T. C. Boville, with various Finance Department employees countersigning on the left. The Boville signature continues for the remainder of the series K and for most of series L. Because of his retirement, Boville's signature was replaced on the plates by that of J. C. Saunders around the beginning of 1921. Before further changes were made. series L was completed, together with series M, N and approximately half of series P, with the Saunders signature.

Late in 1922 it was thought best to begin immediately applying the second signature, that of G. W. Hyndman, by machine, simultaneously impressing the Finance Department seal, because of problems encountered with the ink being used for countersigning by hand. Thus it was that the seal was overprinted on the large TWO counter right of centre, because new plates with the counter removed to make space for the seal were not yet available. The last of series P and part of series R were of the "seal over TWO" variety.

In the spring of 1923 notes with the right hand TWO counter deleted began to be delivered to the Finance Department, where the Hyndman signature and seal were applied by typography. These are known as the "seal only" notes. The remainder of series R was of this type, as were all the notes of series S, which terminated at sheet number 742000. These final "Connaught" $2 notes were received in December 1923.

"Seal over TWO" notes are quite scarce, and care must be exercised in distinguishing them from the less scarce "seal only" notes because the seal almost obliterates the TWO.

Checklist of Prefix Letters for 1914 $2 Dominion Notes

Cat.No.	Denom.	Variety	Serial Numbers	Quantity Printed
DC-22a	$2	"Will Pay.." curved; no hyphen	Boville, r.	A B C
DC-22a-i	$2	"Will Pay.." curved; with hyphen	Boville, r.	D E F G H J K
DC-22b	$2	"Will Pay.." straight	Boville, r.	K L
DC-22c	$2	"Will Pay.." straight	Saunders, r.	L M N P
DC-22d	$2	"Will Pay.." straight, seal over TWO	Hyndman-Saunders	P R
DC-22e	$2	"Will Pay.." straight, seal only	Hyndman-Saunders	R S

Summary of Technical Details

Cat.No.	Denom.	Variety	Series	Serial Numbers	Quantity Printed
DC-22a	$2	"Will Pay..." curved, no hyphen, Boville (no seal)	A	000001-1000000/A,B,C,D	4,000,000
			B	000001-1000000/A,B,C,D	4,000,000
			C	000001-1000000/A,B,C,D	4,000,000
DC-22a-i	$2	"Will Pay..." curved; with hyphen, Boville (no seal)	D	000001-1000000/A,B,C,D	4,000,000
			E	000001-1000000/A,B,C,D	4,000,000
			F	000001-1000000/A,B,C,D	4,000,000
			G	000001-1000000/A,B,C,D	4,000,000
			H	000001-1000000/A,B,C,D	4,000,000
			J	000001-1000000/A,B,C,D	4,000,000
			K	000001- 144113/A,B,C D	Unknown
DC-22b	$2	"Will Pay..." straight; Boville, (no seal)	K	... -1000000/A,B,C D	Unknown
			L	000001-... /A,B,C D	
DC-22c	$2	"Will Pay..." straight; Saunders (no seal)	L	... -1000000/A,B,C D	Unknown
			M	000001-1000000/A,B,C,D	4,000,000
			N	000001-1000000/A,B,C,D	4,000,000
			P	000001- 221821/A,B,C,D	Unknown
DC-22d	$2	"Will Pay..." straight; Hyndman-Saunders (seal over TWO)	P	... -1000000/A,B,C,D	Unknown
			R	000001- 039155/A,B,C,D	Unknown
DC-22e	$2	"Will Pay..." straight; Hyndman-Saunders, (seal only)	R	499839-1000000/A,B,C,D	Unknown
			S	000001- 742000/A,B,C,D	2,968,000

$2 Issue — 1914

DC-22a

Face Design: Duke of Connaught/—/Duchess of Connaught
See varieties
Colour: Black with brown and olive tint

DC-22a-i

Back Design: —/Royal Coat of Arms encircled by the shields of the nine
provinces and maple leaves/—
Colour: Olive green

Issue Date: Engraved: Jan'y 2nd 1914   **Imprint:** American Bank Note
Co. Ottawa

Signatures

Left: mss. various
mss. various
Typed: G.W. Hyndman

Right: Engr.: T.C. Boville
Engr.: J.C. Saunders
Engr.: J.C. Saunders

$2 Issue — 1914

Varieties

Over the black lathework of the centre counter is the wording "WILL PAY TO BEARER ON DEMAND" which appears two different ways:

Curved   Straight

"WILL PAY TO BEARER ON DEMAND"

The seal of the Department of Finance is used during the middle of this issue and is over-printed on, or replaced the right TWO of the centre counter.

TWO at right   Black seal over TWO at right   Black seal only

Cat. No.	Denom.	Variety	Series	G	VG	F	VF	EF	AU	Unc
DC-22a	$2	No seal, "Will pay..." curved, Boville	A,B,C	30.	60.	90.	160.	325.	480.	800.
DC-22a-i	$2	Same, but with hyphen	D,E,F,G H,J,K	15.	30.	45.	80.	160.	250.	425.
DC-22b	$2	No seal, "Will Pay..." straight, Boville	K,L	45.	90.	135.	240.	480.	725.	1,200.
DC-22c	$2	Same, but Saunders	L,M,N,P	35.	70.	105.	185.	375.	550.	925.
DC-22d	$2	Seal over TWO; Hyndman-Saunders	P,R	55.	110.	165.	290.	580.	875.	1,450.
DC-22e	$2	Seal only, Hyndman-Saunders	R,S	40.	80.	120.	210.	425.	650.	1,100

Issue of 1917

The only new issue designed during the First World War, the sixth issue of $1 Dominion notes not unexpectedly has several patriotic and military symbols. The centre of the note face portrays Princess Patricia (1886-1974), daughter of the former Governor General and his wife, T.R.H. the Duke and Duchess of Connaught. The lower part of the portrait is flanked by flags and maple leaves. Princess Patricia lent her name and assistance in raising a regiment designated "Princess Patricia's Light Infantry", designed the regiment's colours, and became its Colonel-in-Chief. The issue date on the notes commemorates the sailing of the "Princess Pat's" for England. Upon her marriage to Admiral Sir Alexander Ramsay, the Princess assumed the name Lady Patricia Ramsay.

As on all $1 Dominion notes since 1897, the back depicts the Centre Block of the Parliament Buildings, although, unlike the previous issues, the view is from inside the front gate. However, the Centre Block no longer existed, having been destroyed by fire on February 3, 1916, with only the Library being saved.

The first notes to be printed in this series have the engraved T. C. Boville signature in the right-hand signature space, with the countersignatures of various Finance Department employees at the left. The notes were printed by the American Bank Note Company, Ottawa, but the face and back imprints were omitted. However, their A. B. N. Co. logo was discreetly hidden away as part of the design on both sides. The logo can be found on the face on the left-hand side directly below the scroll, and on the back it is in the lower left corner close to the scroll work. The series letter follows the sheet number, from which it is separated by a hyphen. Notes of this type correspond to series A, B, C, D, E, F, G and the first part of series H.

It was in 1919, within series H, that the American Bank Note Company imprints were added on instructions from the Department of Finance, and this modified type continued into series J. In the latter part of series J, the series letter was placed ahead of the sheet number, from which it continued to be separated by a hyphen. These notes, still bearing the Boville signature, correspond to late series J, series K, L, M and N, and much of series P. In September 1921 the Boville signature was removed from the plates and replaced by that of J. C. Saunders. With no other changes, the Saunders notes completed series P and continued through series R, S, T, U, V, W, X, Y and Z.

By September 1922, for the first time in an issue of Dominion notes, the alphabet had been exhausted for use as series letters, excepting the letters I, O and Q which were avoided because of their resemblance to the digits 1 and 0. It was decided to start through the alphabet over again, with the series letter still preceding the sheet number, but with the letter "A" following the sheet number, with no hyphen, to indicate that the series letters were being used for the second time.

This procedure had just begun when it was decided to apply the second signature by machine, together with the Finance Department seal. The changeover occurred with sheet A-910500A, in October 1922. Because it was considered desirable to begin machine signing immediately time did not allow for the removal from the plates of the right-hand ONE counter thus the transitional "seal over ONE" variety was created. The seal is in black ink, and the typographed signature is that of G. W. Hyndman, placed in the space designated "COUNTER-SIGNED". These notes correspond to the last of series A, together with all of series B, C, D and E, all of course having the letter "A" after the sheet number. To the right of the seal the series is repeated as A-1, B-1. etc.

In September 1923 notes of the second design appeared, having the right-hand ONE counter omitted. The space in which the typographed Hyndman signature was added was redesignated "FOR COMPTROLLER OF CURRENCY". The "seal only" notes occur in series F, G, H and J, the latter series ending at sheet J-855000A. The final deliveries of the 1917-dated Princess Pat issue were made to the Finance Department in October 1924, several months after the first 1923 King George V notes began to be received. Hoards of all the major varieties have turned up in excellent states of preservation.

Checklist of Prefix Letters for 1917 Dominion Notes

Cat.No.	Denom.	Variety	Signature	Series Letters
DC-23a	$1	No seal, Boville r. Series Letter at end, no imprints	Boville	A B C D E F G H
DC-23a-i	$1	Imprints added	Boville	H J
DC-23a-ii	$1	Series Letter at beginning	Boville	J K L M N P
DC-23b	$1	As above	Saunders	P R S T U V W X Y Z
DC-23b-i	$1	"A" after sheet numbers	Saunders	A
DC-23c	$1	Seal over ONE at right	Hyndman-Saunders	A B C D E
DC-23d	$1	Seal only at right	Hyndman-Saunders	F G H J

Summary of Technical Details

Cat.No.	Denom.	Variety	Series	Serial Numbers	Quantity Printed
DC-23a	$1	No imprints; suffix letter; Boville	A	000001-1000000/A,B,C,D	4,000,000
			B	000001-1000000/A,B,C,D	4,000,000
			C	000001-1000000/A,B,C,D	4,000,000
			D	000001-1000000/A,B,C,D	4,000,000
			E	000001-1000000/A,B,C,D	4,000,000
			F	000001-1000000/A,B,C,D	4,000,000
			G	000001-1000000/A,B,C,D	4,000,000
			H	000001-... /A,B,C,D	Unknown
DC-23a-i	$1	Imprints added, suffix letter, Boville	H	... -1000000/A,B,C,D	Unknown
			J	000001-... /A,B,C,D	Unknown
DC-23a-ii	$1	Prefix letter, Boville	J	... -1000000/A,B,C,D	4,000,000
			K	000001-1000000/A,B,C,D	4,000,000
			L	000001-1000000/A,B,C,D	4,000,000
			M	000001-1000000/A,B,C,D	4,000,000
			N	000001-1000000/A,B,C,D	4,000,000
			P	000001-... /A,B,C,D	Unknown
DC-23b	$1	Prefix letter, Saunders	P	... -1000000/A,B,C,D	Unknown
			R	000001-1000000/A,B,C,D	4,000,000
			S	000001-1000000/A,B,C,D	4,000,000
			T	000001-1000000/A,B,C,D	4,000,000
			U	000001-1000000/A,B,C,D	4,000,000
			V	000001-1000000/A,B,C,D	4,000,000
			W	000001-1000000/A,B,C,D	4,000,000
			X	000001-1000000/A,B,C,D	4,000,000
			Y	000001-1000000/A,B,C,D	4,000,000
			Z	000001-1000000/A,B,C,D	4,000,000
DC-23b-i	$1	Prefix letter, Saunders suffix "A"	A	000001A-910500/A/A,B,C,D	3,642,000
DC-23c	$1	Seal over ONE at right, Hyndman-Saunders	A	910501A-1000000/A/A,B,C,D	358,000
			B	000001A-1000000/A/A,B,C,D	4,000,000
			C	000001A-1000000/A/A,B,C,D	4,000,000
			D	000001A-1000000/A/A,B,C,D	4,000,000
			E	000001A-1000000/A/A,B,C,D	4,000,000
DC-23d	$1	Seal only at right, Hyndman-Saunders	F	000001A-1000000/A/A,B,C,D	4,000,000
			G	000001A-1000000/A/A,B,C,D	4,000,000
			H	000001A-1000000/A/A,B,C,D	4,000,000
			J	000001A- 855000/A/A,B,C,D	4,000,000

DC-23a-ii

Face Design: —/Princess Patricia/—
Colour: Black with green tint

DC-23a-ii

Back Design: —/Parliament Building, view from inside the front gate/—
Colour: Green

Issue Date: Engraved: March 17th
1917

Imprint: American Bank Note
Company Ottawa, face
and back or no imprint

Signatures

Left: mss. various
mss. various
Typed G.W. Hyndman

Right: Engr.: T.C. Boville
Engr.: J.C. Saunders
Engr.: J.C. Saunders

Varieties

The seal of the Department of Finance is used during the middle of this issue and is over-printed on, or replaces the right ONE of the right counter.

ONE at right   **Black seal over ONE at right**   **Black seal only**

Cat. No.	Denom.	Variety	Series	VG	F	VF	EF	AU	Unc
DC-23a	$1	No seal, no imprints, Boville, r.	A,B,C,D, E,F,G,H	15.	25.	45.	90.	135.	225.
DC-23a-i	$1	No seal, imprints, Boville, Suffix letter	H,J	40.	60.	100.	200.	300.	500.
DC-23a-ii	$1	No seal, imprints, Boville, Prefix letter	J,K,L, M,N,P	15.	25.	45.	90.	135.	225.
DC-23b	$1	No seal, Saunders, r.	P,R,S, T,U,V, W,X,Y,Z	15.	25.	45.	90.	135.	225.
DC-23b-i	$1	No seal, Saunders, r., Suffix "A"	A	40.	60.	100.	200.	300.	500.
DC-23c	$1	Seal over ONE, Suffix	A,B,C, "A" D,E	25.	55.	85.	175.	250.	400.
DC-23d	$1	Seal only, Suffix "A"	F,G,H,J	25.	55.	85.	175.	250.	400.

Issue of 1923

25c ISSUE — 1923

The face design of the 25c fractional note was considerably altered from the 1900 issue. The seated Britannia vignette was replaced by a head and torso vignette located in the centre of the note, with a large brown 25 counter at the left and the Department of Finance seal at the right. All notes of this issue correspond to an "A" series (A-1 at right of seal), which was never completed. Only in this third and final issue were the "shinplasters" provided with serial numbers. The second signature was restored. The backs remained unchanged from those of the 1900 issue.

On the first variety of this issue, the words "AUTHORIZED BY R. S. C. CAP. 31" are found above the left-hand signature space. They were issued by the Finance Department despite an earlier decision not to release any notes with this inscription. The notes were numbered in sheets of ten, using check letters A, B, C, D, E, H, J, K, L and M. The check letter is indicated in red prefixing the sheet number. The signatures are those of G. W. Hyndman, typographed at the left, and J. C. Saunders, engraved at the right. The notes were printed bearing the Saunders signature only. After delivery to the Finance Department the Hyndman signature and seal were added. The first plates for this issue were prepared in September 1923.

On the second and subsequent varieties, the words indicating the authorizing legislation were ommitted. The red prefix check letter was removed, and replaced by a black letter engraved to the left of the large brown 25 counter. Three signature varieties exist: G. W. Hyndman-J. C. Saunders, delivered December 1924; S. P. McCavour-J. C. Saunders, delivered intermittently between April 1925 and March 1932; and C. E. Campbell-W. C. Clark, delivered in March 1932. On the final variety, the notes were printed without signatures as a result of the J. C. Saunders signature having been deleted from the plates. Both Campbell and Clark signatures were applied by the Finance Department.

A popular method of collecting these fractional notes is to acquire one of each check letter for each variety, making a total of 40 notes for this issue. Some specialists collect by plate numbers, which are found in the following combinations:

TABLE

PLATE NUMBER COMBINATIONS FOR 1923 ISSUE FRACTIONALS

A. "AUTHORIZED BY R. S. C. CAP. 31" PRESENT

Face Plate #	Back Plate #
1	1, 2
2	1, 2

B. "AUTHORIZED BY R. S. C. CAP. 31" OMITTED
1. Signed G. W. Hyndman

Face Plate #	Back Plate #
1	1, 2
2	1, 2

2. Signed S. P. MacCavour

Face Plate #	Back Plate #'s
1	1, 2
2	1, 2
3	1, 2, 3, 4
4	1, 2, 3, 4
5	3, 4
6	3, 4

3. Signed C. E. Campbell

Face Plate #	Back Plate #'s
7	3, 4
8	3, 4

Summary of Technical Details for 1923

Cat.No.	Variety	Series	Serial Numbers	Qty. Printed
DC-24a	With "Authorized...", Hyndman-Saunders	A	000001-051000/A-M	510,000
DC-24b	Without "Authorized...", Hyndman-Saunders	A	051001-092000/A-M	410,000
DC-24c	Without "Authorized...", McCavour-Saunders	A	092001-605000/A-M	5,130,000
DC-24d	Without "Authorized...", Campbell-Clark	A	605001-700000/A-M	950,000

25c Issue — 1923

DC-24b

Face Design: —/Britannia holding her trident/—
See varieties
Colour: Black with brown tint

DC-24d

Back Design: Lathework and counters
Colour: Green

Issue Date: Engraved: July 2nd 1923

Imprint: Canadian Bank Note
Company Limited

Signatures

Left: Typed C.W. Hyndman
Typed S.P. McCavour
Typed C.E. Campbell

Right: Engr.: J.C. Saunders
Engr.: J.C. Saunders
Typed: W.C. Clark

Varieties

The early notes of this issue carried the supposed authorizing legislation "Revised Statutes of Canada" above the left signature.

 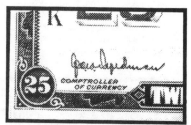

With AUTHORIZED BY R.S.C. CAP. 31.   **Without AUTHORIZED BY R.S.C. CAP. 31.**

Notes of the DC-24a issue come with red check letters A,B,C,D,E,H,J,K,L or M prefixing the sheet number. On catalogue numbers DC-24b, 24c and 24d the check letter is black and is beside the large left counter.

Cat. No.	Denom.	Variety	VG	F	VF	EF	AU	Unc
DC-24a	25c	AUTHORIZED, etc. Hyndman-Saunders	20.	45.	80.	140.	210.	350.
DC-24b	25c	No AUTHORIZED, Hyndman-Saunders	25.	60.	85.	150.	225.	375.
DC-24c	25c	No AUTHORIZED, McCavour-Saunders	4.	9.	17.	30.	45.	75.
DC-24d	25c	No AUTHORIZED, Campbell-Clark	8.	16.	28.	50.	75.	125.

$1 ISSUE 1923

The $1 Dominion notes of 1923 feature a large portrait of King George V, prepared from a photograph. The general layout of the other details on the face of the note bears some resemblance to that of the previous $1 issue. A space was left at the right for the application of the seal by the Finance Department. Various colours of seals were used to facilitate the sorting of notes as they were returned for redemption and destruction. The colours used for sealing were officially designated black, red, blue, green, bronze and purple, although collectors have long been accustomed to calling the latter two "purple-brown" and "lilac" respectively. The scarce purple seal was used to mark a very limited issue of notes printed on experimental paper, as will be explained in detail under the heading "Experimental Issues".

On the backs is found a vignette of the Library of Parliament, the only part of the Centre Block surviving the disastrous fire of February 3, 1916, having been saved by its steel doors. At the time the notes were being designed, however, reconstruction was substantially complete. The new structure resembles the old Centre Block in general outline but is a storey higher and fireproof. The corner stone of the Peace Tower was laid by the Prince of Wales in 1919. The Library of Parliament was badly damaged by fire in 1952, and was reopened in 1956. The printing of the notes was done by the Canadian Bank Note Company, formerly the Ottawa branch of the American Bank Note Company. This change of name seemed advisable in the face of growing Canadian nationalism.

VARIETIES

The notes of this issue are divided into four groups, the group number being found at the right of the seal and in the same colour. For group 1 notes, the 1 is preceded by the series letter, as A-1, B-1, etc. This is a continuation of the practice followed when sealing began on the previous issue. Subsequent groups are identified by a large 2, 3 or 4 found at the right of the seal, but with no letter. The groups are numbered in chronological order as issued, with the exception of the experimental purple seal notes.

The first notes of this issue, belonging to group 1, were delivered to the Finance Department in July 1924. The engraved J. C. Saunders signature was printed on the notes as part of the face plate detail. The typed G. W. Hyndman signature and black seal were applied by the Finance Department prior to distribution of the notes for circulation. Notes of this description were printed in series A, B and C, consisting of 1,000,000 sheets of four notes (distinguished by check letters A, B, C and D) in each series. The series letter is printed in red, prefixed to the sheet number by a hyphen.

In March 1925 the Hyndman signature typographed in the left-hand space was replaced by that of S. P. McCavour, and the seal colour was changed to red. Again, three series of one million sheets each were produced. This was followed by blue, green and bronze seals respectively, each appearing on three series of one million sheets.

The first notes of group 2 were delivered in the summer of 1927. The McCavour-Saunders signature combination was still in use. The application of seals of a particular colour was extended over four series rather than three as previously. Black seals were used for the first four series of this group, series S, T, U and V, and red seals were used for the completion of the alphabet.

In 1927 a new $1 note design was being modelled by the Canadian Bank Note Company, which featured a portrait of Sir John A. Macdonald engraved from a photograph. Possibly it was intended to introduce this design after the series letters of the King George issue progressed to the end of the alphabet, a point which was actually reached in November 1928.

However, the problem of devising additional new serial numbers was solved without replacing the existing design, and using a different procedure from that followed for the Princess Pat issue. The series letters began at "A" again, with the sheets numbered from 1000001 to 6000000 with the hyphen removed, so that each new series consisted of five million sheets of four notes, rather than one million as previously. Still within group 2 and with the McCavour-Saunders signature combination, delivery of the "A" series with a blue seal began in November 1928. This was followed by the "B" series with a bronze seal beginning in October 1929 and the "C" series with a green seal in May 1930. This brought to an end the group 2 part of the issue.

Group 1 reappeared briefly in May and June of 1931 with the release of the experimental purple seal notes. This time the numbering continued past 6000000, still within series "C". Most of the notes bear the McCavour-Saunders signature combination, although the Comptroller of Currency, C. E. Campbell, had instructed the bank note company to delete the engraved Saunders signature the previous February, Mr. Saunders having died in 1930. However the presses were shut down only one at a time to make the alteration on the plates, to avoid the temporary layoffs that would be brought on by idling all of the presses at once. Consequently a part of the new notes delivered as late as July 1931 continued to bear the obsolete Saunders signature, to the exasperation of Mr. Campbell.

Some of the purple seal notes were delivered without any signature to the Finance Department, where the signatures of C. E. Campbell and Watson Sellar, the Acting Deputy Minister of Finance, were applied by typography. The changeover number for this signature combination was 6386001. Surprisingly, the McCavour-Saunders signatures reappeared at some point. No documentation has been found indicating the precise changeover for this reversion, but an examination of the numbers of surviving notes indicated that it was 649----. The experimental purple seal issue ended at sheet number 6525000, and series "C" was terminated at the same time. These experimental notes mark the last time that seals coloured other that black were used on $1 Dominion notes.

In July 1931 the first notes of group 3 were supplied to the Finance Department. All notes of this group are in series "D", which consisted of nine million sheets numbered from 1000001 to 10000000. The first few sheets, up to number 1195000, have the McCavour-Saunders signatures, while all the others have the Campbell-Sellar signatures. The series "D" notes have black seals.

Delivery of the group 4 notes began in February 1933. This group is distinguished by the introduction of the Campbell-Clark signature combination. Again, the notes were delivered unsigned, with both signatures and the seal being typed on by the Finance Department. A full series "E", consisting of nine million sheets numbered 1000001 to 10000000, was issued. This was followed by only half a million sheets in Series "F", numbered from 1000001 to 1500000. These were the final $1 Dominion notes, and the last delivery was made in January 1935. Series "F" was terminated at this point because the large Dominion notes were about to be superseded by the small size notes of the newly-formed Bank of Canada.

EXPERIMENTAL ISSUES

Before 1929, all Canadian bank notes and Dominion notes were being printed on paper supplied by Crane & Co. of Dalton, Mass. A 1907 report on tests applied to the paper revealed that it was satisfactory and durable. During the First World War I, difficulties arose with the Crane paper which led to a shorter circulation life of the notes. By 1925 some Crane paper of altered composition, having less linen and about 25% cotton, was used for Dominion notes on a trial basis, found satisfactory and approved for general use. With this change, the Canadian Bank Note Co. expected the notes to survive from one to one and a half years in circulation. This was considered quite acceptable, especially since the growing motor garage business was resulting in increased soiling of notes.

However, a Canadian paper source was considered desirable, and the government entered into discussions with the Howard Smith Paper Co. of Beauhamois, P.Q. (Subsequently known as the Domtar Corp.). The company was given to understand that an order would be forthcoming when they could furnish a paper that could stand up reasonably well under mechanical tests.

Comparison tests performed on the Crane and Smith bank note papers revealed that they were essentially equal in terms of folding strength and resistance to rubbing. The Crane paper was almost white; Smith's was a cream shade. Crane's paper absorbed moisture more readily, making it easier to wet for printing. The Howard Smith paper seemed sufficiently promising to justify being tested in circulation. On March 14, 1928 the Finance Department instructed the Canadian Bank Note Company to prepare 100,000 sheets of $1 Dominion notes on Howard Smith paper. The 400,000 notes were to be distributed in various provinces for wear tests. The number of notes was kept low to minimize the cost to the government if the test proved unsuccessful.

Whether the full order of 100,000 sheets was printed is uncertain, but it is known that at least 78,500 sheets were completed in June 1929 having sheet numbers 1000001-1078500 in series "B", group 2 (bronze seal). The paper was noted by the bank note company to take a better finish than Crane's paper, although it was darker in colour. There were some problems with the new paper. Bank note company employees had to sort the sheets to remove those containing knots or strings, comprising about 4% of the total. An extra step was required to wet the paper in preparation for printing because of its resistance to water. The Howard Smith company agreed to assume the resulting extra costs. The Finance Department early in 1931 pronounced itself satisfied with the results of the experiment, and it was considered even more appropriate to use the Canadian product to provide employment opportunities during the depression.

A larger experimental test, consisting of 500,000 sheets to be printed on Howard Smith paper, was ordered before the final decision would be made. In fact 525,000 sheets were printed and delivered in the spring of 1931. These were identified with a purple seal, a colour not used on any other Dominion notes, to make them easier to sort out for the wear test studies.

On the basis of all the tests, the Finance Department instructed the Canadian Bank Note Company to switch over to Howard Smith paper for all Dominion notes. The last sheet of $1 notes to be printed on Crane paper was number 1195000 in series "D" (group 3, black seal). This was, coincidentally, the last sheet bearing the McCavour-Saunders signature combination.

Checklist of Prefix Letters for 1923 $1 Dominion Notes

GROUP 1

Cat.No.	Denom.	Signatures	Seal	Series Letters
DC-25a	$1	Hyndman-Saunders	Black	A B C
DC-25b	$1	McCavour-Saunders	Red	D E F
DC-25c	$1	McCavour-Saunders	Blue	G H J
DC-25d	$1	McCavour-Saunders	Green	K L M
DC-25e	$1	McCavour-Saunders	Bronze	N P R

GROUP 2

Cat.No.	Denom.	Signatures	Seal	Series Letters
DC-25f	$1	McCavour-Saunders	Black	S T U V
DC-25g	$1	McCavour-Saunders	Red	W X Y Z
DC-25h	$1	McCavour-Saunders	Blue	A
DC-25i	$1	McCavour-Saunders	Bronze	B
DC-25j	$1	McCavour-Saunders	Green	C

GROUP 1: EXPERIMENTAL

Cat.No.	Denom.	Signatures	Seal	Series Letters
DC-25k	$1	McCavour-Saunders	Purple	C
DC-25l	$1	Campbell-Sellar	Purple	C

GROUP 3

Cat.No.	Denom.	Signatures	Seal	Series Letters
DC-25m	$1	McCavour-Saunders	Black	D
DC-25n	$1	Campbell-Sellar	Black	D

GROUP 4

Cat.No.	Denom.	Signatures	Seal	Series Letters
DC-25o	$1	Campbell-Clark	Black	E F

Summary of Technical Details

Cat.No.	Group	Signature	Seal	Series	Serial Numbers	Qty. Printed
DC-25a	1	Hyndman-Saunders	Black	A	000001-1000000/A,B,C,D	4,000,000
DC-25a	1	Hyndman-Saunders	Black	B	000001-1000000/A,B,C,D	4,000,000
DC-25a	1	Hyndman-Saunders	Black	C	000001-1000000/A,B,C,D	4,000,000
DC-25b	1	McCavour-Saunders	Red	D	000001-1000000/A,B,C,D	4,000,000
DC-25b	1	McCavour-Saunders	Red	E	000001-1000000/A,B,C,D	4,000,000
DC-25b	1	McCavour-Saunders	Red	F	000001-1000000/A,B,C,D	4,000,000
DC-25c	1	McCavour-Saunders	Blue	G	000001-1000000/A,B,C,D	4,000,000
DC-25c	1	McCavour-Saunders	Blue	H	000001-1000000/A,B,C,D	4,000,000
DC-25c	1	McCavour-Saunders	Blue	J	000001-1000000/A,B,C,D	4,000,000
DC-25d	1	McCavour-Saunders	Green	K	000001-1000000/A,B,C,D	4,000,000
DC-25d	1	McCavour-Saunders	Green	L	000001-1000000/A,B,C,D	4,000,000
DC-25d	1	McCavour-Saunders	Green	M	000001-1000000/A,B,C,D	4,000,000
DC-25e	1	McCavour-Saunders	Bronze	N	000001-1000000/A,B,C,D	4,000,000
DC-25e	1	McCavour-Saunders	Bronze	P	000001-1000000/A,B,C,D	4,000,000
DC-25e	1	McCavour-Saunders	Bronze	R	000001-1000000/A,B,C,D	4,000,000
DC-25f	2	McCavour-Saunders	Black	S	000001-1000000/A,B,C,D	4,000,000
DC-25f	2	McCavour-Saunders	Black	T	000001-1000000/A,B,C,D	4,000,000
DC-25f	2	McCavour-Saunders	Black	U	000001-1000000/A,B,C,D	4,000,000
DC-25f	2	McCavour-Saunders	Black	V	000001-1000000/A,B,C,D	4,000,000
DC-25g	2	McCavour-Saunders	Red	W	000001-1000000/A,B,C,D	4,000,000
DC-25g	2	McCavour-Saunders	Red	X	000001-1000000/A,B,C,D	4,000,000
DC-25g	2	McCavour-Saunders	Red	Y	000001-1000000/A,B,C,D	4,000,000
DC-25g	2	McCavour-Saunders	Red	X	000001-1000000/A,B,C,D	4,000,000
DC-25h	2	McCavour-Saunders	Blue	A	1000001-6000000/A,B,C,D	20,000,000
DC-25i	2	McCavour-Saunders	Bronze	B	1000001-6000000/A,B,C,D	20,000,000
DC-25j	2	McCavour-Saunders	Green	C	1000001-6000000/A,B,C,D	20,000,000
DC-25k	1	McCavour-Saunders	Purple	C	6000001-6386000/A,B,C,D	
DC-25k	1	McCavour-Saunders	Purple	C	649... -6525000/A,B,C,D	1,644,000 +
DC-25l	1	Campbell-Sellar	Purple	C	6386001-649... /A,B,C,D	416,000 +
DC-25m	3	McCavour-Saunders	Black	D	1000001-1195000/A,B,C,D	780,000
DC-25n	3	Campbell-Sellar	Black	D	1195001-10000000/A,B,C,D	35,220,000
DC-25o	4	Campbell-Clark	Black	E	1000001-10000000/A,B,C,D	36,000,000
DC-25o	4	Campbell-Clark	Black	F	1000001-1500000/A,B,C,D	2,000,000

$1 Issue — 1923

DC-25a

Face Design: —/King George V/—
Colour: Black with green tint

DC-25a

Back Design: —/Library of Parliament/—
Colour: Green
Issue Date: Engraved: July 2nd
1923

Imprint: Canadian Bank Note
Company, Limited on
face and back

Signatures
Left: Typed C.W. Hyndman
Typed S.P. McCavour
Typed C.E. Campbell
Typed C.E. Campbell

Right: Engr.: J.C. Saunders
Engr.: J.C. Saunders
Typed Watson Sellar
Typed W.C. Clark

Varieties

In the Face Design: The Seal of the Department of Finance was printed in the following colours: Black, red, blue, green, bronze or purple.

DC-25n

Purple Seal

Cat. No.	Denom.	Variety	Series	G	VG	F	VF	EF	AU	Unc
DC-25a	$1	Hyndman-Saunders Black seal. Group 1.	A,B,C	20.	40.	60.	100.	200.	300.	500.
DC-25b	$1	McCavour-Saunders Red seal. Group 1.	D,E,F	15.	30.	45.	70.	140.	210.	350.
DC-25c	$1	McCavour-Saunders Blue seal. Group 1.	G,H,J	12.	25.	40.	65.	130.	195.	325.
DC-25d	$1	McCavour-Saunders Green seal. Group 1.	K,L,M	12.	25.	40.	65.	130.	195.	325.
DC-25e	$1	McCavour-Saunders Bronze seal. Group 1.	N,P,R	12.	25.	40.	65.	130.	195.	325.
DC-25f	$1	McCavour-Saunders Black seal. Group 2.	S,T,U,V	10.	20.	35.	60.	120.	180.	300.
DC-25g	$1	McCavour-Saunders Red seal. Group 2.	W,X,Y,Z	10.	20.	35.	60.	120.	180.	300.
DC-25h	$1	McCavour-Saunders Blue seal, Group 2.	A	8.	17.	30.	55.	110.	165.	275.
DC-25i	$1	McCavour-Saunders Bronze seal. Group 2.	B	8.	17.	30.	55.	110.	165.	275.
DC-25j	$1	McCavour-Saunders Green seal. Group 2.	C	8.	17.	30.	55.	110.	165.	275.
DC-25k	$1	McCavour-Saunders Purple seal. Group 1.	C*	65.	130.	200.	360.	725.	1,100.	1,800.
DC-25l	$1	Campbell-Sellar Purple seal. Group 1.	C*	90.	180.	270.	475.	950.	1,450.	2,400.
DC-25m	$1	McCavour-Saunders Black seal. Group 3.	D**	55.	115.	170.	300.	600.	900.	1,500.
DC-25n	$1	Campbell-Sellar Black seal. Group 3.	D	6.	13.	20.	37.	75.	110.	185.
DC-25o	$1	Campbell-Clark Black seal. Group 4.	E,F	6.	13.	20.	37.	75.	110.	185.

* Do not confuse with the commoner bronze seal. Purple seals only occur with C-1 to the right of the seal.

** Do not confuse with the commoner group 2 variety. DC-25m notes only occur with the numeral 3 to the right of the seal.

$2 ISSUE 1923

This denomination features as its central vignette the portrait of the Prince of Wales, who reigned briefly in 1936 as King Edward VII. The photograph which was the basis of the portrait was selected in the summer of 1922, and proofs of the notes were approved in July 1923. The portrait was engraved by Mr. Savage of the American Bank Note Co. in New York City, who received praise from the Finance Department for the high quality of his work. In 1924 the photographer who took the picture from which the engraving was made threatened to sue for infringement of copyright. This was an oversight on the part of the Canadian Bank Note Co. and an amicable settlement was sought.

A different kind of controversy was aroused by the back of the note. The Dominion Coat of Arms was engraved from a photograph of an official drawing supplied by the Department of the Secretary of State. After the plates were engraved and a large quantity of notes issued, certain details were altered by the State Department. It was too late to make any changes in the notes. A Toronto newspaper discovered the discrepancy and criticized the Canadian Bank Note Co.

Like the $1 notes, the 1923 $2 notes are divided into four groups. Group 1 notes have the series letter and numeral 1, separated by a hyphen, following the seal and in the same colour as the seal. The other groups carry a large coloured numeral 2, 3 or 4, to the right of the seal. The groups are numbered in chronological order, as issued.

The first notes of group 1 were delivered to the Finance Department in November 1923. These have a black seal and bear the typed signature of G. W. Hyndman on the left and the engraved signature of J. C. Saunders on the right. These notes completed series "A" and "B", of 1,000,000 sheets each. The series letter is found in red, prefixing the sheet number, as well as to the right of the seal. In March 1925 the typed signature of G. W. Hyndman was replaced by that of S. P. McCavour. Two series of McCavour-Saunders notes were printed with each of seal colours, red, blue, green and bronze. By this point, ten million sheets (or forty million notes) had been printed in group 1, which then terminated.

Group 2 began in February 1929. Two series were printed with each of black, red and blue seal colours. In June 1931, during the production of blue seal notes in series "S", the J. C. Saunders signature was removed from the plates, and the notes were subsequently delivered unsigned to the Finance Department. There the typographed signatures of C. E. Campbell replacing S. P. McCavour, and Watson Sellar replacing J. C. Saunders, were applied along with the seal. The changeover began with sheet number S-194001. This signature change also coincided precisely with the changeover from Crane paper to Howard Smith paper for the $2 notes. Group 2 ended with series "S" in February 1932.

Group 3 notes, as well as those of group 4, were printed with black seals only. Group 3 contained three series on one million sheets, series T, U and V. During series V there was another signature change, with W. C. Clark replacing Watson Sellar in the right-hand signature space. Again, both Campbell and Clark signatures were typographed.

Group 4 notes, consisting of series W and X only, were first delivered in June 1933. Series X was terminated after 850,000 sheets in January 1935, to make way for the introduction of the notes of the Bank of Canada.

Checklist of Prefix Letters for 1923 $2 Dominion Notes

GROUP 1

Cat.No.	Denom.	Signatures	Seal	Series Letters
DC-26a	$2	Hyndman-Saunders	Black	A B
DC-26b	$2	McCavour-Saunders	Red	C D
DC-26c	$2	McCavour-Saunders	Blue	E F
DC-26d	$2	McCavour-Saunders	Green	G H
DC-26e	$2	McCavour-Saunders	Bronze	J K

GROUP 2

Cat.No.	Denom.	Signatures	Seal	Series Letters
DC-26f	$2	McCavour-Saunders	Black	L M
DC-26g	$2	McCavour-Saunders	Red	N P
DC-26h	$2	McCavour-Saunders	Blue	R S
DC-26i	$2	Campbell-Sellar	Blue	S

GROUP 3

Cat.No.	Denom.	Signatures	Seal	Series Letters
DC-26j	$2	Campbell-Sellar	Black	T U V
DC-26k	$2	Campbell-Clark	Black	V

GROUP 4

Cat.No.	Denom.	Signatures	Seal	Series Letters
DC-26l	$2	Campbell-Clark	Black	W X

Summary of Technical Details

Cat.No.	Group	Signatures	Seal	Series	Serial Numbers	Qty. Printed
DC-26a	1	Hyndman-Saunders	Black	A	000001-1000000/A,B,C,D	4,000,000
DC-26a	1	Hyndman-Saunders	Black	B	000001-1000000/A,B,C,D	4,000,000
DC-26b	1	McCavour-Saunders	Red	C	000001-1000000/A,B,C,D	4,000,000
DC-26b	1	McCavour-Saunders	Red	D	000001-1000000/A,B,C,D	4,000,000
DC-26c	1	McCavour-Saunders	Blue	E	000001-1000000/A,B,C,D	4,000,000
DC-26c	1	McCavour-Saunders	Blue	F	000001-1000000/A,B,C,D	4,000,000
DC-26d	1	McCavour-Saunders	Green	G	000001-1000000/A,B,C,D	4,000,000
DC-26d	1	McCavour-Saunders	Green	H	000001-1000000/A,B,C,D	4,000,000
DC-26e	1	McCavour-Saunders	Bronze	J	000001-1000000/A,B,C,D	4,000,000
DC-26e	1	McCavour-Saunders	Bronze	K	000001-1000000/A,B,C,D	4,000,000
DC-26f	2	McCavour-Saunders	Black	L	000001-1000000/A,B,C,D	4,000,000
DC-26f	2	McCavour-Saunders	Black	M	000001-1000000/A,B,C,D	4,000,000
DC-26g	2	McCavour-Saunders	Red	N	000001-1000000/A,B,C,D	4,000,000
DC-26g	2	McCavour-Saunders	Red	P	000001-1000000/A,B,C,D	4,000,000
DC-26h	2	McCavour-Saunders	Blue	R	000001-1000000/A,B,C,D	4,000,000
DC-26h	2	McCavour-Saunders	Blue	S	000001- 194000/A,B,C,D	776,000
DC-26i	2	Campbell-Sellar	Blue	S	194001-1000000/A,B,C,D	3,224,000
DC-26j	3	Campbell-Sellar	Black	T	000001-1000000/A,B,C,D	4,000,000
DC-26j	3	Campbell-Sellar	Black	U	000001-1000000/A,B,C,D	4,000,000
DC-26j	3	Campbell-Sellar	Black	V	000001-600712/A,B,C,D	Unknown
DC-26k	3	Campbell-Clark	Black	V	786100-1000000/A,B,C,D	4,000,000
DC-26l	4	Campbell-Clark	Black	W	000001-1000000/A,B,C,D	4,000,000
DC-26l	4	Campbell-Clark	Black	X	000001- 850000/A,B,C,D	3,400,000

DC-26

Face Design: —/Edward, Prince of Wales in uniform of the Welsh Guards/—
See varieties
Colour: Black with olive green tint

DC-26

Back Design: —/Coat of Arms of Canada/—
Colour: Olive green

Issue Date: Engraved: June 23rd
1923

Imprint: Canadian Bank Note
Company Limited on
face and back

Signatures

Left: Typed C.W. Hyndman
Typed S.P. McCavour
Typed C.E. Campbell
Typed C.E. Campbell

Right: Engr.: J.C. Saunders
Engr.: J.C. Saunders
Typed Watson Sellar
Typed W.C. Clark

Varieties

In the Face Design: The Seal of the Department of Finance was printed in the following colours: Black, red, blue, green or bronze.

Cat. No.	Denom.	Variety	Series	G	VG	F	VF	EF	AU	Unc
DC-26a	$2	Hyndman-Saunders Black seal. Group 1.	A,B	30.	65.	100.	175.	350.	525.	875.
DC-26b	$2	McCavour-Saunders Red seal. Group 1.	C,D	20.	45.	70.	120.	240.	360.	600.
DC-26c	$2	McCavour-Saunders Blue seal. Group 1.	E,F	20.	45.	70.	120.	240.	360.	600.
DC-26d	$2	McCavour-Saunders Green seal, Group 1.	G,H	25.	55.	85.	150.	300.	450.	750.
DC-26e	$2	McCavour-Saunders Bronze seal. Group 1.	J,K	25.	55.	85.	150.	300.	450.	750.
DC-26f	$2	McCavour-Saunders Black seal. Group 2.	L,M	25.	55.	85.	150.	300.	450.	750.
DC-26g	$2	McCavour-Saunders Red seal. Group 2.	N,P	20.	45.	70.	120.	240.	360.	600.
DC-26h	$2	McCavour-Saunders Blue seal. Group 2.	R,S	25.	50.	80.	140.	280.	425.	700.
DC-26i	$2	Campbell-Sellar Blue seal. Group 2.	S	25.	50.	80.	140.	280.	425.	700.
DC-26j	$2	Campbell-Sellar Black seal. Group 3.	T,U,V	12.	25.	40.	75.	150.	225.	375.
DC-26k	$2	Campbell-Clark Black seal. Group 3.	V	20.	40.	60.	100.	200.	300.	500.
DC-26l	$2	Campbell-Clark Black seal. Group 4.	W,X	15.	30.	45.	80.	160.	240.	400.

Issue of 1924

Queen Mary (1867-1953) was the wife of King George V. She was originally engaged to his elder brother, the wayward Duke of Clarence, but married George after the Duke's untimely death. She lived through the reign of two of her sons, Edward VIII and George VI, and the first year of her grandaughter Queen Elizabeth II.

Work on the engraving of the portrait of Queen Mary was in progress in March 1924, when the difficulty with the copyright protecting the Prince of Wales portrait used on the $2 note erupted. The Finance Department wished to avoid a recurrence of the problem with the $5 denomination, so the legal question was carefully checked before further work was done on the portrait. The engraver was probably Mr. Woodhull of the American Bank Note Co. in New York City, where all Canadian Bank Note Co. portrait engraving for Dominion notes was being done at that time. The note is dated May 26, 1924 in honour Queen Victoria's birthday.

The back depicts the East Block of the Parliament Buildings, engraved from a photograph. The general layout of the $5 note conforms to the 1923 $1 and $2 notes. They were printed in blue, distinguishing them from the other denominations.

The Department of Finance had little need for $5 notes on a continuing basis, the needs of commerce for that denomination being largely met by the chartered bank issues. When, in October 1931, an order was given for stocks of $5 notes, it was a seven year hiatus. Only then were the plates for the Queen Mary $5 notes prepared, there having been no previous orders for the notes. The die for the vignette had been put away since being engraved in 1924. The immedite need for the notes was met in 1931 by running off a small final batch of the 1912 "train" notes. Production of the Queen Mary $5 notes began as soon as the plates were ready. Altogether 500,000 sheets of Queen Mary $5 notes were printed, all in series "A". The total production was completed and delivered between late October 1931 and February 1932. The signatures, those of C. E. Campbell and Watson Sellar, were both typed onto the notes along with the seal by the Finance Department. They were the same signatures as those being applied to the $1 and $2 notes at that time.

The Finance Department delayed release of the Queen Mary notes, possibly because a new issue of small-size Dominion notes was then being contemplated (which never became a reality). They were finally put into circulation in 1934, just before the introduction of the Bank of Canada notes and the withdrawal of Dominion notes.

A survey of the sheet numbers of existing notes suggests that only about a third of the modest total printed were ever released for circulation. It is not surprising then, that collectors have long found the Queen Mary $5 to be a very elusive note. Those notes which have turned up are generally in the more attractive grades.

Summary of Technical Details

Cat.No.	Denom.	Variety	Series	Serial Numbers	Quantity Printed
DC-27	$5		A	000001-500000/A,B,C,D	2,000,000

*Approximately one-third of these were issued for circulation.

$5 Issue — 1924

DC-27

Face Design: —/H.M. Queen Mary in official court dress of consort/Department of Finance seal
Colour: Black with blue tint

DC-27

Back Design: —/Parliament Buildings, view of the East Block/—
Colour: Blue

Issue Date: Engraved: May 26th 1924   **Imprint:** Canadian Bank Note Company, Limited on face and back

Signatures
Left: Typed C.E. Campbell   **Right:** Typed Watson Sellar

Cat. No.	Denom.	Series	G	VG	F	VF	EF	AU	Unc
DC-27	$5	A	125.	250.	370.	650.	1,300.	1,950.	3,250.

Issues of 1925

In March 1925 the Department of Finance was experiencing difficulties related to the circulation of the 1911 issue $500 and $1000 notes. It was decided to proceed quickly with a new issue and to withdraw the old notes for accounting.

The portraits of King George V and Queen Mary used on the $500 and $1000 notes were the same as those on the $1 and $5 notes respectively, being from the same dies. The portrait-denomintion combinations were interchanged from the 1911 issue, possibly to facilitate sorting. The notes were called "Bearer Notes", since they were inscribed "Will pay to the bearer", to distinguish them from the Bank Legals. The backs have no vignettes, consisting essentially of lathework and counters.

No seal was applied to these high denomination notes, and the area at the right of the portrait reserved on the lower values for the departmental seal was occupied by an additional large counter. Neither engraved nor typed signatures were printed on the notes. Both the signature and countersignature were applied by hand in Ottawa by various officials of the Finance Department.

The previous issue of these denominations had "SERIES A" engraved on the faces on both sides of the vignette. This was deleted on the 1925 issue, but the series letter was continued as a prefix to the serial number. There were no check letters either, the notes being numbered individually rather than by the sheet.

Only one 4/on face plate was engraved for each denomination, in May 1925. An order for 40,000 notes of the $500 denomination and 30,000 of the $1,000 value had been placed the previous March. In July all of the $500 notes and six thousand of the $1,000 notes were delivered to the Finance Department. It may be supposed that the remaining $1,000 notes followed in due course, but the delivery date is not known.

When the new notes became available the Finance Department instructed its Assistant Receivers General to withdraw the 1911 issue notes immediately, and to ask the banks to exchange any notes in their possession.

Summary of Technical Details

Cat.No.	Denom.	Variety	Series	Serial Numbers	Quantity Printed
DC-28	$500		A	000001-040000	40,000
DC-29	$1000	A		000001-030000	30,000*

*Assumed, on the basis of order of March 7, 1925.

$500 Issue — 1925

DC-28

Face Design: —/King George V/—
Colour: Black with brown tint

DC-28

Back Design: Lathework, counters and Dominion name
Colour: Brown
Issue Date: Engraved: Jany 2nd 1925   **Imprint:** Canadian Bank Note
Company, Limited on
face and back

Signatures
Left: mms. various   **Right:** mss. various

Cat. No.	Denom.	Series	G	VG	F	VF	EF	AU	Unc
DC-28	$500	A	700.	900.	1,100.	1,500.	2,500.	3,500.	5,500.
DC-28	$500	A						SPECIMEN	1,000.

$1,000 Issue — 1925

DC-29

Face Design: —/Queen Mary/—
Colour: Black with orange tint

DC-29

Back Design: Lathework, counters and Dominion name
Colour: Orange

Issue Date: Engraved: Jany 2nd 1925   **Imprint:** Canadian Bank Note
Company, Limited

Signatures

Left: mss. various   **Right:** mss. various

Cat. No.	Denom.	Series	G	VG	F	VF	EF	AU	Unc
DC-29	$1,000.	A	1,200.	1,400.	1,600.	2,000.	3,000.	4,000.	6,000.
DC-29	$1,000.	A						SPECIMEN	1,000.

The Proposed Small Size Dominion Note Issue

In January 1931 the Comptroller of Currency, C. E. Campbell, inquired of the Canadian Bank Note Company what savings might be expected if the size of Dominion notes were reduced to the dimensions adopted by the United State in 1928. Economic considerations had prompted the American move, bank note paper being very costly. In March a model of the $1 face was assembled, and a projected cost of $49.75 per thousand notes was worked out.

The following January the reduction in Dominion note size was again being considered, and models of a $2 face and backs of both $1 and $2 denominations were ordered. The distinctive colours of each denomination were to be retained, and the date line was specified to read "OTTAWA 2nd July 1932" on the tint. Then further work was suddenly ordered to be suspended, to permit the notes to be redesigned on a shorter and wider format than the U.S. notes. In February 1932 a further alteration was requested, to bilingual notes. The bank note company feared that greatly increasing the amount of information to be printed on a note would reduce its protection against counterfeiting, which depended on large, well-executed portraits.

The project of another Dominion note issue was shelved as the establishment of a central bank was coming under active consideration. Such a bank would eventually assume all of the note issuing functions.

Bank Legals

Bank legals were very large denomination notes which were not issued for general circulation. Sometimes referred to as "bank specials", these notes were held by the chartered banks as a convenient form for the Dominion note reserves required by the bank act in lieu of gold. They were exchanged between banks in settlement of their cash balances with each other.

When the Bank of Canada began its operations in 1935, the cash deposits each chartered bank was required to lodge with the central bank, replacing Dominion note reserves, were made with the bank legals. The bank legals thereafter ceased to have any purpose and were withdrawn.

None are available to collectors and they are included here for reference only.

Denominations	Date	Vignette
$500	July 2, 1896	Marquis of Lorne
$1,000	July 2, 1896	Queen Victoria
$5,000	July 2, 1896	Sir John A. Macdonald
$1,000	Jan. 2,	1901 Lord Roberts
$5,000	Jan. 2, 1901	Queen Victoria
$5,000	Jan. 2, 1918	Queen Victoria
$50,000	Jan. 2, 1918	King George and Queen Mary
$1,000	Jan. 2, 1924	Lord Roberts
$5,000	Jan. 2, 1924	Queen Victoria
$50,000	Jan. 2, 1924	King George and Queen Mary

BANK OF CANADA ISSUES

The Bank of Canada came into being through the work of a typically Canadian institution, a Royal Commission. The majority report of the Royal Commission on Banking and Currency, brought down in September 1933, favoured the establishment of a central bank in Canada. The chartered banks were not enthusiastic but pledged their co-operation. The bill to incorporate the Bank of Canada was brought in by the Conservative government of R. B. Bennett during the 1934 session of Parliament. The capital of the bank was set at $5,000,000, divided into shares of $50 each which were offered for sale to the public in September 1934 and largely oversubscribed despite the fact that no individual or corporation was allowed to hold more than fifty shares.

The Liberals under W. L. M. King were returned to power in 1935. They had opposed private ownership of the bank from the start and promised to "nationalize" it as part of their election platform. This King typically proceeded to do by halves. In 1936 he had an additional $5,100,000 in class "B" shares created and sold to the Finance Department, giving the government majority ownership and effective control. In 1938 King "nationalized" the bank again. This time the class "A" shares held by the public were bought up by the government for $59.20 each plus accrued dividends. The capital was reduced to the original $5,000,000, with all of the shares now owned by the government.

Although the government owns all of the shares in the Bank of Canada, it remains relatively free of political interference and is prepared to offer the government skilled and impartial advise on monetary policy. However, monetary policy in a democratic country must conform to the wishes of the elected government, which has the power to issue orders to the bank. This was illustrated by the celebrated dispute of J. E. Coyne with the Diefenbaker administration, which resulted in the governor's position being declared vacant because of Coyne's refusal to co-operate.

The Bank of Canada was not established to engage in ordinary banking business with the public in competition with the chartered banks. The central bank accepts deposits from other banks and will if necessary lend them money. When the Bank of Canada was set up, the chartered banks were required to deposit 5% of their own deposit liabilities with the central bank, replacing the reserves formerly held in gold and Dominion notes. The old Bank Legals and gold previously held as part of their reserves were paid in to the Bank of Canada to comply with this regulation.

The Bank of Canada was originally required to hold gold reserves equal to 25% of its note and bank deposit liabilities. This requirement disappeared early in World War II since the existing gold available was inadequate to cover the necessary expansion of the money supply. Since then the Bank of Canada notes have not had any gold backing.

The bank commenced business on March 11, 1935. The first set of officers, appointed by the government, included G. F. Towers, formerly with the Royal Bank of Canada, as Governor; J. A. C. Osborne, on loan from the Bank of England, as Deputy Governor; and L. P. St. Amour, formerly with La Banque Canadienne Nationale, as Assistant Deputy Governor. The bank was given responsibility for management of the currency and the national debt. The head office was established in Ottawa, with agencies in every province. The bank assumed liability for the Dominion notes in circulation, which it undertook to replace by its own small-size notes in denominations of $1, $2, $5, $10, $20, $25, $50, $100, $500 and $1000.

The chartered banks were required to reduce their note circulation to 25% of their paid-up capital over the next ten years. The 1944 revision of the bank act then prohibited the issue or reissue of any chartered bank's own notes after January 1, 1945. The last issue by a chartered bank was the $5 Royal Bank issue of 1943. The notes of the chartered banks were withdrawn and as of January 1, 1950, liability for all outstanding chartered bank notes was assumed by the Bank of Canada. The issue of chartered bank notes for circulation outside of Canada was still permitted to a maximum of 10% of the paid-up capital under the 1944 act, but even that was ended under the 1954 revision of the bank act. During January 1950 the ten Canadian chartered banks paid over to the Bank of Canada the balances outstanding in their note circulation accounts as at December 31, 1949, amounting to $13,302,046.60. (Since that time over $5,000,000 in notes of the chartered banks have been turned in for redemption, leaving about

$8,000,000 outstanding). This was the final step in the 15-year programme under which the Bank of Canada assumed the entire issuing function of the country and wrote "finis" to an important, sometimes tempestuous, chapter of Canadian banking history.

Issues of 1935

When the Bank of Canada opened for business on March 11, 1935, it issued its own notes in denominations of $1, $2, $5, $10, $20, $50, $500 and $1000. The notes were of the small 6 x 2 7/8 inch format which resulted in a saving of both bank note paper and ink. This Bank of Canada issue consisted of separate unilingual English and French notes. As might be expected, most of the French notes were sent to the Bank of Canada agency in Montreal for distribution, although most of the other agencies received a small supply as well.

For the first time since 1897 the British American Bank Note Company received a contract for printing government paper currency. British American printed the $2, $5 and $10 notes while the Canadian Bank Note Company printed the remaining denominations, including the $25 commemorative note. Thereafter both security printers participated in the production of Bank of Canada notes.

The regular issue notes up to the $100 denomination feature different members of the Royal Family on the left, with a large numeral counter in the middle and the Bank of Canada seal on the right. The $500 and $1000 notes portray former Prime Ministers Macdonald and Laurier respectively. The backs of all denominations of these regular issue notes depict various allegorical scenes. The portrait of King George V on the $1 note was engraved from a photograph by Lafayette Ltd. of London, England. The art work for the back was done by A. E. Foringer. H. P. Dawson engraved the Queen Mary portrait on the $2 and the face portraits and backs for the $5 and $10 denominations.

DETAILS OF THE PRINTING

The lower denominations were printed from 24/on plates, with the last few sheets needed to complete an order, called make-up sheets, being from 4/on plates. The higher denominations were printed 12/on, with make-ups again being 4/on. Howard Smith bank note paper was used, in which green planchettes were embedded as a security device.

Sheets were numbered in red, twice on the face of each note, in groups of four notes each with the same number. For each sheet number there were four distinguishing black check letters, A, B C and D. For the most part there was only a single series for each denomination in each language, Series "A" for English and series "F" for French. However, the "A" series of English $1 notes, consisting of ten million "sheets" of four notes, was completed and a "B" series begun.

The notes were delivered by the bank note companies without signatures and seals. These were added by the letterpress method by Bank of Canada personnel, using plates prepared by the Royal Canadian Mint. The signatures applied were those of J. A. C. Osborne, Deputy Governor, and G. F. Towers, Governor. Because the signing was done after the notes were printed, the positions of the signatures tend to vary. Black seals only were used, and in all cases the numeral 1 appears to the right of the seal, identifying the notes as being from Group 1. Since the notes were issued over a relatively short time span, the group number never progressed beyond 1. Large seals were used on the $1, $2, $5, $10, $25 and the lower numbered $20 notes, while the higher numbered $20 notes and the denominations of $50 and up had small seals.

CIRCULATION AND WITHDRAWAL

The $25 commemorative note was the first to be withdrawn from circulation. On May 18, 1937, it was decided to cancel both new and issued $25 notes as they were acquired by the Bank of Canada agencies. By August 1942 only 1,920 of these notes had escaped withdrawl and cancellation. In the summer of 1937 it was intended to continue issuing the other denominations until all of the stocks on hand had been used up. Shortly afterwards, there arose some trouble with the 1935 $2 notes which were being confused with the 1937 $5 notes because both were blue in colour. Consequently the 1935 $2 note was ordered withdrawn from circulation as quickly as possible and on September 18, 1937 about 3,900,000 new, unissued $2 notes were taken out of stock for destruction. In February 1938 stocks of unissued notes of other denominations, except for the $1000 notes, were also destroyed, with 824,500 unissued $5 and 3,565,000 unissued $10 notes consigned to the furnaces. The withdrawal of $1, $5 and $10 notes began that month, and the $20, $50, $100 and $500 notes began to be withdrawn the following July. The $500 denomination was permanently retired, and at the time of preparation of this edition only 48 of these were outstanding.

The $1000 notes enjoyed by far the greatest longevity. It was not until January 1952 that the old 1935-dated $1000 notes were superseded by 1937-dated notes. This denomination was used primarily by the chartered banks. The old notes were not recalled from the banks but neither were they reissued from the Bank of Canada agencies.

Summary of Technical Details

Cat.No.	Denom.	Variety	Printer	Series	Serial Numbers	Qty. Printed
BC-1	$1	English	CBN	A	0000001-10000000/A,B,C,D	40,000,000
BC-1	$1	English	CBN	B	0000001- 5078000/A,B,C,D	20,312,000
BC-2	$1	French	CBN	F	0000001- 3799000/A,B,C,D	15,196,000
BC-3	$2	English	BABN	A	000001- 5585000/A,B,C,D	22,340,000
BC-4	$2	French	BABN	F	000001- 1325000/A,B,C,D	5,300,000
BC-5	$5	English	BABN	A	000001- 1535000/A,B,C,D	6,140,000
BC-6	$5	French	BABN	F	000001- 750000/A,B,C,D	3,000,000
BC-7	$10	English	BABN	A	000001- 1250000/A,B,C,D	5,000,000
BC-8	$10	French	BABN	F	000001- 387500/A,B,C,D	1,550,000
BC-9a	$20	English, (large seal)	CBN	A	000001-... /A,B,C,D	
BC-9b	$20	English, (small seal)	CBN	A	... - 250675/A,B,C,D	1,002,700
BC-10	$20	French	CBN	F	000001- 050625/A,B,C,D	202,500
BC-11	$25	English	CBN	A	000001- 035000/A,B,C,D	140,000
BC-12	$25	French	CBN	F	000001- 005000/A,B,C,D	20,000
BC-13	$50	English	CBN	A	000001- 32750/A,B,C,D	131,000
BC-14	$50	French	CBN	F	000001- 08125/A,B,C,D	32,500
BC-15	$100	English	CBN	A	000001- 21875/A,B,C,D	87,500
BC-16	$100	French	CBN	F	000001- 04375/A,B,C,D	17,500
BC-17	$500	English	CBN	A	000001- 05225/A,B,C,D	20,900
BC-18	$500	French	CBN	F	000001- 01250/A,B,C,D	5,000
BC-19	$1000	English	CBN	A	000001- 16625/A,B,C,D	66,500
BC-20	$1000	French	CBN	F	000001- 01900/A,B,C,D	7,600

$1 Issue — 1935

BC-1

Face Design: King George V/—/—
Colour: Black with green tint

BC-1

Back Design: —/Agriculture allegory: seated female with
agricultural products/—
Colour: Green

Issue Date: Engraved: 1935

Imprint: Canadian Bank Note
Company, Limited on
face and back

Signatures
Left: Typed J.A.C. Osborne   **Right:** Typed G.F. Towers

Cat. No.	Denom.	Variety	Series	VG	F	VF	EF	AU	Unc
BC-1	$1	English	A	10.	15.	23.	45.	90.	135.
BC-1	$1	English	B	10.	16.	25.	50.	100.	150.
BC-2	$1	French	F	15.	23.	35.	70.	140.	210.

$2 Issue — 1935

BC-4

Face Design: Queen Mary/—/—
Colour: Black with blue tint

BC-3

Back Design: —/Transportation allegory: Mercury with ships trains, and planes/—
Colour: Blue

Issue Date: Engraved: 1935

Imprint: British American Bank Note Co Ltd Ottawa on face and back

Signatures
Left: Typed J.A.C. Osborne   **Right:** Typed G.F. Towers

Cat. No.	Denom.	Variety	Series	VG	F	VF	EF	AU	Unc
BC-3	$2	English	A	17.	25.	45.	90.	135.	200.
BC-4	$2	French	F	30.	45.	90.	180.	360.	700.

$5 Issue — 1935

BC-6

Face Design: Prince of Wales/—/—
Colour: Black with orange tint

BC-5

Back Design: —/Electric Power allegory: Seated male with symbols
of electricity/—
Colour: Orange

Issue Date: Engraved: 1935

Imprint: British American Bank
Note Co Ltd Ottawa on
face and back

Signatures
Left: Typed J.A.C. Osborne

Right: Typed G.F. Towers

Cat. No.	Denom.	Variety	Series	VG	F	VF	EF	AU	Unc
BC-5	$5	English	A	30.	45.	70.	140.	280.	425.
BC-6	$5	French	F	55.	85.	150.	300.	450.	700.

$10 Issue — 1935

BC-7

Face Design: Princess Mary /—/—
Colour: Black with dark purple tint

BC-7

Back Design: —/Harvest allegory: Seated female with fruits of harvest
Colour: Dark purple

Issue Date: Engraved: 1935

Imprint: British American Bank Note Co Ltd Ottawa on face and back

Signatures
Left: Typed J.A.C. Osborne

Right: Typed G.F. Towers

Cat. No.	Denom.	Variety	Series	VG	F	VF	EF	AU	Unc
BC-7	$10	English	A	35.	50.	90.	180.	270.	450.
BC-8	$10	French	F	60.	90.	160.	320.	480.	800.

$20 Issue — 1935

BC-10

Face Design: Princess Elizabeth/—/—
See varieties
Colour: Black with rose tint

BC-9b

Back Design: —/Toiler allegory: Kneeling male exhibiting the produce of the field
of the Spirit of Agriculture/—
Colour: Rose
Issue Date: Engraved: 1935

Imprint: Canadian Bank Note
Company, Limited on
face and back

Signatures
Left: Typed J.A.C. Osborne

Right: Typed G.F. Towers

Varieties

$20 English Issue Face Design:

Large Bank of Canada Seal   Small Bank of Canada Seal

Cat. No.	Denom.	Variety	Series	VG	F	VF	EF	AU	Unc
BC-9a	$20	English, (large seal)	A	125.	185.	325.	650.	950.	1,600.
BC-9b	$20	English, (small seal)	A	150.	225.	400.	800.	1,200.	2,000.
BC-10	$20	French	F	190.	285.	500.	1,000.	1,500.	2,500.

THE $25 COMMEMORATIVE NOTE

The $25 note was a special commemorative issue marking the Silver Jubilee of the reign of King George V. These notes were printed in separate English and French versions like the regular issue notes of 1935, but they do not, strictly speaking, form part of the first issue. They have a different issue date, May 6, 1935, whereas the other denominations are simply dated ISSUE OF 1935. The regnal dates 1910-1935 appear at the top, and under the portraits appear the inscription TWENTY-FIFTH ANNIVERSARY OF THE ACCESSION OF H.M. KING GEORGE V. This denomination is the only one having two portraits, those of King George V and Queen Mary, and these are located in the centre, with the large denominational counter occurring on the left. Instead of an allegorical vignette, the back depicts Windsor Castle as seen from across the Thames River.

Some difficulty was experienced with the King's crown, which was too large to fit in the frame. This was solved by allowing the upper part of the crown to cross over the frame, from which it protrudes so far as to divide the words PAY and TO. The Bank of Canada agencies were instructed to release the notes on May 2, four days before their printed issue date.

Of the 160,000 $25 notes issued, a total of 1,840 were still outstanding at the time of preparation of this edition.

$25 Issue — 1935

BC-12

Face Design: —/King George V and Queen Mary/—
Colour: Black with royal purple tint

BC-11

Back Design: —/Windsor Castle/—
Colour: Royal Purple

Issue Date: Engraved: May 6th 1935   **Imprint:** Canadian Bank Note
                                                        Company, Limited on
                                                        face and back

Signatures
Left: Typed J.A.C. Osborne   **Right:** Typed G.F. Towers

Cat. No.	Denom.	Variety	Series	VG	F	VF	EF	AU	Unc
BC-11	$25	English	A	225.	350.	600.	1,200.	1,800.	2,700.
BC-12	$25	French	F	325.	500.	900.	1,800.	2,700.	4,000.

$50 Issue — 1935

BC-14

Face Design: Prince Albert, Duke of York/—/—
Colour: Black with brown tint

BC-14

Back Design: —/Modern inventions allegory: Seated female with symbols of radio broadcasting/—
Colour: Brown

Issue Date: Engraved: 1935

Imprint: Canadian Bank Note Company, Limited on face and back

Signatures
Left: Typed J.A.C. Osborne

Right: Typed G.F. Towers

Cat. No.	Denom.	Variety	Series	VG	F	VF	EF	AU	Unc
BC-13	$50	English	A	200.	300.	525.	1,050.	1,575.	2,400.
BC-14	$50	French	F	300.	450.	675.	1,350.	2,025.	3,000.

$100 Issue — 1935

BC-15

Face Design: Prince Henry. Duke of Gloucester/—/—
Colour: Black with dark brown tint

BC-15

Back Design: —/Commerce and Industry allegory: Seated male showing ship to child, harbour scene and blast furnace in background
Colour: Dark brown

Issue Date: Engraved: 1935

Imprint: Canadian Bank Note Company, Limited on face and back

Signatures
Left: Typed J.A.C. Osborne

Right: Typed G.F. Towers

Cat. No.	Denom.	Variety	Series	VG	F	VF	EF	AU	Unc
BC-15	$100	English	A	300.	450.	675.	1,350.	2,025.	3,000.
BC-16	$100	French	F	325.	500.	900.	1,800.	2,700.	4,000.

$500 Issue — 1935

BC-17

Face Design: Sir John A. Macdonald/—/—
Colour: Black with brown tint

BC-17

Back Design: —/Fertility allegory: Seated female with sickle/—
Colour: Brown

Issue Date: Engraved: 1935

Imprint: Canadian Bank Note Company Limited on face and back

Signatures
Left: Typed J.A.C. Osborne

Right: Typed G.F. Towers

Cat. No.	Denom.	Variety	Series	VG	F	VF	EF	AU	Unc
BC-17	$500	English	A	1,400.	2,100.	3,150.	4,700.	7,000.	10,500.
BC-18	$500	French	F	1,600.	2,400.	3,600.	5,400.	8,000.	12,000.

$1000 Issue — 1935

BC-19

Face Design: Sir Wilfrid Laurier/—/—
Colour: Black with olive green tint

BC-19

Back Design: —/Security allegory: Kneeling female shielding her child/—
Colour: Olive green

Issue Date: Engraved: 1935

Imprint: Canadian Bank Note Company, Limited on face and back

Signatures
Left: Typed J.A.C. Osborne

Right: Typed G.F. Towers

Cat. No.	Denom.	Variety	Series	VG	F	VF	EF	AU	Unc
BC-19	$1000	English	A	1,100.	1,150.	1,225.	1,400.	1,600.	1,900.
BC-20	$1000	French	F	1,200.	1,300.	1,450.	1,800.	2,200.	2,800.

Issues of 1937

The 1937 issue of the Bank of Canada was the first to be bilingual. It had proven too expensive to prepare separate English and French emissions of the 1935 issue. The denominations and text are in English on the left side and French on the right. All notes are the same size as those of the 1935 issue (6" long by 2 7/8" wide). Denominations in this issue consist of $1, $2, $5, $10, $20, $50, $100 and $1000, and although there was some feeling on the part of the public that there should also be a 25-cent fractional note, it was not sufficiently widespread to receive serious consideration from Bank officials. Both the Canadian and British American Bank Note Companies were receiving orders for 1937 notes as early as October 1936, during the reign of King Edward VIII. At least some of the denominations being prepared would have borne his portrait. The new prefix system of numbering explained below (see "Serial Numbers and Signatures") was to go into effect for this issue. When Edward VIII abdicated in December 1936, he was succeeded by his brother, the Duke of York, who reigned as King George VI. King Edward's portrait was replaced by that of King George, using the same vignette as on the $50 note of 1935. The King's portrait was moved from the left to the centre of the note, and was used on all denominations from $1 to $50. The portrait of Sir John A. Macdonald used at the left of the 1935 $500 note was moved to the centre of the $100 denomination, while Sir Wilfred Laurier continued to appear on the $1000 note, also being moved to the centre.

Like the portraits on the faces, the allegorical vignettes on the backs of the notes of the 1937 issue were the same as those used in 1935, although in some cases they were used on different denominations. The old $20 back vignette was abandoned and replaced on the new $20 notes by that of the former $500 denomination. The $2 and $10 back vignettes were interchanged from their 1935 situations. The backs were also made bilingual, English on the left and French on the right; the counters were made larger and the lathework was altered. A number of denominations also underwent colour changes.

The 1937 issue was released for circulation on July 21, 1937 in denominations from $1 to $100. Originally it was intended to put all remaining stocks of the 1935 issue into circulation except for the $25 denomination, and to withhold notes of the 1937 issue except when they were specifically requested. This plan was scuttled by the confusion which arose between the 1935 $2 and the 1937 $5, both of which were blue, causing the destruction of the reserves of the 1935 $2 notes. Most other denominations of the 1935 issue were phased out by July 1938. Thus the 1937 issue displaced the former issue somewhat earlier than had been anticipated, increasing the cost to the Bank of Canada. To replace the stocks of unused 1935 notes which had been destroyed, the British American Bank Note Company printed $2, $5 and $10 notes at a much reduced rate. The 1937 $1000 notes were the last to be released for circulation, when they finally superseded the 1935 $1000 notes in January 1952. The "new" $1000 notes had been printed in 1937 and had been kept in the reserve stockpile of the Bank of Canada over the years, as indicated by the Osborne-Towers signatures.

The paper used for the issue was again supplied by Howard Smith Paper Co. of Montreal. The bank note paper used in 1937 was composed of 75% highest grade linen and 25% cotton. Its ability to withstand the stresses of circulation was so great the the notes were usually withdrawn because of having become excessively soiled rather than because of wear. The use of watermarked paper was contemplated but rejected. As with the previous issue, the paper was manufactured containing green planchettes to increase the security of the notes against counterfeiting. Planchettes were also used in the production of notes for the chartered banks with a different colour assigned for the use of each bank. In 1941 the linen content was reduced to 50%, because of the necessity of conservation during wartime. For the same reason the use of chlorine in bleaching the paper was reduced, as was the amount of titanium oxide, a paper brightener. This resulted in a decrease in overall brightness of the paper.

SERIAL NUMBERS AND SIGNATURES

Beginning with the 1937 issue, the Bank of Canada adopted a two-letter prefix, written as a fraction. The lower letter was the denominational letter, reserved for use on one specific denomination. The upper letter designated the series and could be used on any denomination. Within each series, notes were numbered from 0000001 to 10000000 with the number printed twice in red on the face of each note. Since each note on the sheet had a different number, there was no need for using check letters.

Ordinarily the series letters used were A,B,C,D,E,H,J,K,L,M,N,O,R,S,T,U,W,X,Y and Z, a total of twenty letters, corresponding to 20 series to 10000000 notes each. Occasionally letters were added to this list or deleted (see checklist of prefix letters). Thus each denominational letter could usually be used for 200,000,000 notes.

If more notes were needed, a new denominational letter was chosen. By September 1941 it was clear that the end of the use of the "A" denominational letter for the $1 notes was imminent. It was decided to give the next twenty series the denominational letter "L", which in turn lasted until the end of 1946 when the letter "M" was begun. The "M" group contained series F and G, letters which had apparently not been authorized, so this group consisted of 22 series. The final $1 group, the "N" group, probably began in 1951. The only other denominations for which the demand exceeded twenty series of 10,000,000 notes each, the $2, $5 and $10, all exhausted their first denominational letters (B, C and D) in 1949 and were then assigned letters R, S and T respectively.

The lower denominations were printed from 24/on plates (3 across, 8 down) and 12/on plates were used for the higher denominations. To print the small quantities required to finish the last few notes of an order, 4/on plates were used. The notes were not numbered consecutively on each sheet but were "skip-numbered". This means that the notes on a given sheet received numbers which differed by 1,000, so that when a stock of 1,000 sheets was cut, the notes automatically formed "bricks" of 1,000 consecutively-numbered notes. From 1937 to 1940 the Canadian Bank Note Company "skipped" $1 sheets by five thousands, which made bricks of 5,000 $1 notes, but then began printing in limits of 1,000 as for the other denominations.

The 1937 issue consists of three sets of signatures. The first Deputy Governor of the Bank of Canada, J. A. C. Osborne, resigned on September 14, 1938. He had been "on loan" from the Bank of England since 1934. His successor was Donald Gordon, whose signature was applied on notes printed from November 1938. The unused numbers in series which were in progress when the signature change occurred were cancelled, so that Gordon's signature appeared together with the new series prefix letters. In the case of the $1 and $2 notes however, the last series receiving the Osborne signature had been completed so that no discontinuity occurred in the numbering of these denominations.

James E. Coyne was appointed Deputy Governor on January 1, 1950 to replace Donald Gordon who had resigned to become President of Canadian National Railways. This time the last series of each denomination to receive the Gordon signature was not terminated, but instead completed with the Coyne signature. The changeover occurred within each series of numbers which are listed in the Summary of Technical Details. Graham F. Towers remained Governor of the Bank of Canada throughout the entire issue, and his signature is found in the right hand space on all of the notes.

The $1 Face Plate Modification

All notes of the 1937 issue were delivered to the Bank of Canada without signatures. There the signatures were applied by letterpress using a plate prepared from signature dies made by the Royal Canadian Mint. Considerable difficulty was encountered in 1937 with the $1 notes with respect to registration of the signatures. Because the signatures and the signature panel were almost the same height, there was little margin for error if the signatures were not to appear either too high or too low. The Canadian Bank Note Company suggested a reduction in the size of the signatures, an option which did not appeal to Bank of Canada officials. They in turn felt that if the sheets were trimmed with very uniform margins the problem would be eliminated. Although the bank note company tried to improve its margins, the necessary precision was difficult to attain because the notes were printed wet and shrank during drying. Finally in mid-1938 a suggestion was made to rearrange the $1 note leaving about 3/32" more space in the signature panel. The proposal was approved because it would solve the problem of signing the notes while not being noticeable to the general public. The face plate was modified accordingly and specimens of the new $1 notes with the wide signature panel were approved in November 1938. The first of these notes produced for circulation were given prefix letters K/A and were probably released early in 1939.

Checklist of Prefix Letters

Cat.No.	Denom.	Signatures	Denom. Letter	Series Letter
BC-21a	$1	Osborne-Towers	A	A B C D E
BC-21b	$1	Gordon-Towers (NP)	A	H J
BC-21c	$1	Gordon-Towers (WP)	A	K L M N O R S T U W X Y Z
BC-21c	$1	Gordon-Towers (WP)	L	A B C D E H J K L M N O R S T U W X Y Z
BC-21c	$1	Gordon-Towers (WP)	M	A B C D E F G H J K L M N O
BC-21d	$1	Coyne-Towers	M	O R S T U W X Y Z
BC-21d	$1	Coyne-Towers	N	A B C D E H J L M N O R S T U W
BC-22a	$2	Osborne-Towers	B	A B
BC-22b	$2	Gordon-Towers	B	C D E H J K L M N O R S T U W X Y Z
BC-22c	$2	Coyne-Towers	B	Z
BC-22c	$2	Coyne-Towers	R	A B C D E H J K L
BC-23a	$5	Osborne-Towers	C	A
BC-23b	$5	Gordon-Towers	C	B C D E H J K L M N O R S T U W X
BC-23c	$5	Coyne-Towers	C	X Y Z
BC-23c	$5	Coyne-Towers	S	A B C D E H
BC-24a	$10	Osborne-Towers	D	A
BC-24b	$10	Gordon-Towers	D	B C D E H J K L M N O R S T U W X Y Z
BC-24c	$10	Coyne-Towers	D	Z
BC-24c	$10	Coyne-Towers	T	A B C D E H J K L M
BC-25a	$20	Osborne-Towers	E	A
BC-25b	$20	Gordon-Towers	E	B C D E H
BC-25c	$20	Coyne-Towers	E	H J K L
BC-26a	$50	Osborne-Towers	H	A
BC-26b	$50	Gordon-Towers	H	B
BC-26c	$50	Coyne-Towers	H	B
BC-27a	$100	Osborne-Towers	J	A
BC-27b	$100	Gordon-Towers	J	B
BC-27c	$100	Coyne-Towers	J	B
BC-28	$1000	Osborne-Towers	K	A

Summary of Technical Details

Cat.No.	Denom.	Variety	Printer	Prefixes	Numbers	Qty. Printed
BC-21a	$1	Osborne-Towers	CBN	A/A-E/A	0000001-10000000	50,000,000
BC-21b	$1	Gordon-Towers (NP)	CBN	H/A-J/A	0000001-10000000	20,000,000
BC-21c	$1	Gordon-Towers (WP)	CBN	K/A-N/M	0000001-10000000	460,000,000
BC-21c	$1	Gordon-Towers (WP)	CBN	O/M	0000001-2840000	2,840,000
BC-21d	$1	Coyne-Towers	CBN	O/M	2840001-10000000	7,160,000
BC-21d	$1	Coyne-Towers	CBN	R/M-U/N	0000001-10000000	230,000,000
BC-21d	$1	Coyne-Towers	CBN	W/N	0000001-2408000	2,408,000
BC-22a	$2	Osborne-Towers	BABN	A/B-B/B	0000001-10000000	20,000,000
BC-22b	$2	Gordon-Towers	BABN	C/B-X/B	0000001-10000000	170,000,000
BC-22b	$2	Gordon-Towers	BABN	Z/B	0000001-4000000	4,000,000
BC-22c	$2	Coyne-Towers	BABN	Z/B	4000001-10000000	6,000,000
BC-22c	$2	Coyne-Towers	BABN	A/R-K/R	0000001-10000000	80,000,000
BC-22c	$2	Coyne-Towers	BABN	L/R	0000001-5668000	5,668,000
BC-23a	$5	Osborne-Towers	BABN	A/C	0000001-8824500(est.)	8,824,500 (est.)
BC-23b	$5	Gordon-Towers	BABN	B/C-W/C	0000001-10000000	160,000,000
BC-23b	$5	Gordon-Towers	BABN	X/C	0000001-5200000	5,200,000
BC-23c	$5	Coyne-Towers	BABN	X/C	5200001-10000000	4,800,000
BC-23c	$5	Coyne-Towers	BABN	Y/C-E/S	0000001-10000000	70,000,000
BC-23c	$5	Coyne-Towers	BABN	H/S	Unknown-6915536	7,000,000 (est.)
BC-24a	$10	Osborne-Towers	BABN	A/D	0000001-6356500(est.)	6.356,500 (est.)
BC-24b	$10	Gordon-Towers	BABN	B/D-Y/D	0000001-10000000	180,000,000
BC-24b	$10	Osborne-Towers	BABN	Z/D	0000001-5000000	5,000,000
BC-24c	$10	Coyne-Towers	BABN	Z/D	5000001-10000000	5,000,000
BC-24c	$10	Coyne-Towers	BABN	A/T-L/T	0000001-10000000	90,000,000
BC-24c	$10	Coyne-Towers	BABN	M/T	0000001-2960000	2,960,000
BC-25a	$20	Osborne-Towers	CBN	A/E	0000001-1622000(est.)	1,622,000 (est.)
BC-25b	$20	Gordon-Towers	CBN	B/E-E/E	0000001-10000000	40,000,000
BC-25b	$20	Gordon-Towers	CBN	H/E	0000001-1500000	1,500,000
BC-25c	$20	Coyne-Towers	CBN	H/E	1500001-10000000	8,500,000
BC-25c	$20	Coyne-Towers	CBN	J/E-K/E	0000001-10000000	20,000,000
BC-25c	$20	Coyne-Towers	CBN	L/E	0000001-1416000	1,416,000
BC-26a	$50	Osborne-Towers	CBN	A/H	0000001-0100000	100,000
BC-26b	$50	Gordon-Towers	CBN	B/H	0000001-4200000	4,200,000
BC-26c	$50	Coyne-Towers	CBN	B/H	4200001-5300000	1,100,000
BC-27a	$100	Osborne-Towers	CBN	A/J	0000001-0070000	70,000
BC-27b	$100	Gordon-Towers	CBN	B/J	0000001-4170000	4,170,000
BC-27c	$100	Coyne-Towers	CBN	B/J	4170001-5070000	900,000
BC-28	$1000	Osborne-Towers	CBN	A/K	0000001-0015000	15,000

$1 Issue — 1937

BC-21d

Face Design: —/King George VI/—
See varieties
Colour: Black with green tint

BC-21d

Back Design: —/Agriculture allegory: Seated female with agricultural products/—
Colour: Green

Issue Date: Engraved: 2nd JAN 1937

Imprint: Canadian Bank Note Company, Limited on face and back

Signatures

Left: Typed J.A.C. Osborne
Typed D. Gordon
Typed J.E. Coyne

Right: Typed G.F. Towers
Typed G.F. Towers
Typed G.F. Towers

Varieties

The Face Design with the narrow and wide signature panel can be easily identified by the spacing of the King's portrait medallion from the note's border. The narrow signature variety has a wider space between the top of the Kings' portrait and the top border. The wide signature panel variety has a very narrow space in the same area.

BC-21b

Narrow Signature Panel

BC-21c

Wide Signature Panel

Cat. No.	Denom.	Variety	VG	F	VF	EF	AU	Unc
BC-21a	$1	Osborne-Towers	8.	15.	30.	45.	65.	100.
BC-21b	$1	Gordon-Towers(NP)	8.	15.	30.	45.	65.	100.
BC-21c	$1	Gordon-Towers(WP)	3.	4.	6.	9.	13.	20.
BC-21d	$1	Coyne-Towers	3.	4.	6.	9.	13.	20.

$2 Issue — 1937

BC-22a

Face Design: —/King George VI/—
Colour: Black with red-brown tint

BC-22a

Back Design: —/Harvest allegory: Seated female with fruits of harvest/—
Colour: Red-brown

Issue Date: Engraved: 2nd JAN 1937

Imprint: British American Bank
Note Company Limited
on face and back

Signatures

Left: Typed J.A.C. Osborne
Typed D. Gordon
Typed J.E. Coyne

Right: Typed G.F. Towers
Typed G.F. Towers
Typed G.F. Towers

Cat. No.	Denom.	Variety	VG	F	VF	EF	AU	Unc
BC-22a	$2	Osborne-Towers	15.	25.	50.	80.	120.	180.
BC-22b	$2	Gordon-Towers	8.	10.	13.	20.	30.	45.
BC-22c	$2	Coyne-Towers	8.	10.	13.	20.	30.	45.

$5 Issue — 1937

BC-23c

Face Design: —/King George VI/—
Colour: Black with blue tint

BC-23c

Back Design: —/Electric Power allegory: Seated male with symbols of electricity/—
Colour: Blue

Issue Date: Engraved: 2nd JAN 1937

Imprint: British American Bank Note Company Limited on face and back

Signatures

Left: Typed J.A.C. Osborne
Typed D. Gordon
Typed J.E. Coyne

Right: Typed G.F. Towers
Typed G.F. Towers
Typed G.F. Towers

Cat. No.	Denom.	Variety	VG	F	VF	EF	AU	Unc
BC-23a	$5	Osborne-Towers	50.	75.	125.	200.	300.	450.
BC-23b	$5	Gordon-Towers	8.	10.	13.	20.	30.	45.
BC-23c	$5	Coyne-Towers	10.	13.	16.	25.	35.	50.

$10 Issue — 1937

BC-24b

Face Design: —/King George VI/—
Colour: Black with purple tint

BC-24b

Back Design: -/Transportation allegory: Mercury with ships, trains and planes/—
Colour: Purple

Issue Date: Engraved: 2nd JAN 1937

Imprint: British American Bank Note Company Limited on face and back

Signatures
Left: Typed J.A.C. Osborne
Typed D. Gordon
Typed J.E. Coyne

Right: Typed G.F. Towers
Typed G.F. Towers
Typed G.F. Towers

Cat. No.	Denom.	Variety	VG	F	VF	EF	AU	Unc
BC-24a	$10	Osborne-Towers	35.	50.	60.	90.	135.	200.
BC-24b	$10	Gordon-Towers	8.	10.	13.	20.	30.	45.
BC-24c	$10	Coyne-Towers	8.	10.	13.	20.	30.	45.

$20 Issue — 1937

BC-25b

Face Design: —/King George VI/—
Colour: Black with olive green tint

BC-25b

Back Design: —/Fertility allegory: Seated female with sickle/—
Colour: Olive green

Issue Date: Engraved: 2nd JAN 1937

Imprint: Canadian Bank Note Company, Limited on face and back

Signatures

Left: Typed J.A.C. Osborne
Typed D. Gordon
Typed J.E. Coyne

Right: Typed G.F. Towers
Typed G.F. Towers
Typed G.F. Towers

Cat. No.	Denom.	Variety	VG	F	VF	EF	AU	Unc
BC-25a	$20	Osborne-Towers	90.	110.	145.	220.	325.	500.
BC-25b	$20	Gordon-Towers	20.	22.	25.	35.	55.	80.
BC-25c	$20	Coyne-Towers	20.	22.	25.	40.	60.	90.

$50 Issue — 1937

BC-26c

Face Design: —/King George VI/—
Colour: Black with orange tint

BC-26c

Back Design: —/Modern Inventions allegory: Seated female with symbols of
radio broadcasting/—
Colour: Orange

Issue Date: Engraved: 2nd JAN 1937   **Imprint:** Canadian Bank Note
Company, Limited on
face and back

Signatures
Left: Typed J.A.C. Osborne   **Right:** Typed G.F. Towers
Typed D. Gordon   Typed G.F. Towers
Typed J.E. Coyne   Typed G.F. Towers

Cat. No.	Denom.	Variety	VG	F	VF	EF	AU	Unc
BC-26a	$50	Osborne-Towers	250.	375.	550.	975.	1,500.	2,250.
BC-26b	$50	Gordon-Towers	50.	55.	60.	90.	135.	200.
BC-26c	$50	Coyne-Towers	50.	55.	60.	90.	135.	200.

$100 Issue — 1937

BC-27a

Face Design: —/Sir John A. Macdonald/—
Colour: Black with brown tint

BC-27a

Back Design: —/Commerce and Industry allegory: Seated male showing ship to child, harbour scene and blast furnace in background/—
Colour: Brown

Issue Date: Engraved: 2nd JAN 1937

Imprint: Canadian Bank Note Company, Limited on face and back

Signatures
Left: Typed J.A.C. Osborne
Typed D. Gordon
Typed J.E. Coyne

Right: Typed: G.F. Towers
Typed: G.F. Towers
Typed: G.F. Towers

Cat. No.	Denom.	Variety	VG	F	VF	EF	AU	Unc
BC-27a	$100	Osborne-Towers	140.	175.	225.	350.	500.	750.
BC-27b	$100	Gordon-Towers	120.	125.	130.	145.	165.	200.
BC-27c	$100	Coyne-Towers	125.	130.	140.	160.	200.	250.

$1000 Issue — 1937

BC-28

Face Design: —/Sir Wilfrid Laurier/—
Colour: Black with rose pink tint

BC-28

Back Design: —/Security allegory: Kneeling female shielding her child/—
Colour: Rose pink

Issue Date: Engraved: 2nd JAN 1937

Imprint: Canadian Bank Note Company, Limited on face and back

Signatures
Left: Typed J.A.C. Osborne

Right: Typed G.F. Towers

Cat. No.	Denom.	Variety	VG	F	VF	EF	AU	Unc
BC-28	$1000	Osborne-Towers	1,000.	1,000.	1,150.	1,300.	1,475.	1,600.

Issue of 1954

The third issue of the Bank of Canada, and the second to have a bilingual format, was prepared following the untimely death in 1952 of King George VI and released in 1954. The new notes measured 6 x 2 3/4 inches, slightly narrower than the issue they replaced. The portrait of Queen ELizabeth II, appearing on the faces of all denominations from $1 to $1000, was placed at the right-hand side where it was less susceptible to wear caused by folding than the previous centrally placed portrait. George Gundersen of the British American Bank Note Company engraved the portrait.

The allegorical vignettes on the backs of the previous issues were abandoned in favour of Canadian landscapes. The rural scene on the $2 back and the Rocky Mountain scene on the $10 back were engraved by H. P. Dawson. Gordon Yorke engraved the northern river scene on the $5 back. The latter two engravers were also employed by the British American Bank Note Company.

The printing contracts were again divided between the Canadian Bank Note Company, which produced $1, $5, $20, $50, $100 and $1,000 notes, and the British American Bank Note Company which printed $1, $2, $5 and $10 notes. The issue was terminated over the interval 1970 to 1976 because the alphabet had practically been exhausted as a source of denominational letters, every letter but Q having been employed for this purpose. In addition, dangerous counterfeits had become a serious problem, particularly affecting the $50 and $100 denominations. The final signature varieties of these denominations were quickly replaced by the new multi-coloured notes, resulting in their present scarcity.

THE "DEVIL'S FACE" NOTES

On the earliest notes of the 1954 issue, highlighted areas of the Queen's hair produced the illusion of a leering demonic face behind her ear. This was not the result of an error, nor was it, as some have asserted, the prank of an IRA sympathizer at the bank note company. It was merely the faithful reproduction of the original photograph. The portrait of the Queen with the "Devil's Face" outlined in her hair generated almost instant controversy. The portrait was modified by darkening the highlights in the hair and thus removing the shading which had resulted in the "devil". The modification of the face plates was made for most denominations in 1956, except for the $1000 denomination which was modified several years later.

Devil's Face Portrait

Modified Portrait

PREFIXES AND NUMBERING

The procedure for numbering notes which was initiated on the 1937 issue was continued, with slight modifications, on the 1954 issue. Once again the number was preceded by two prefix letters, written as a fraction. The upper letter was the series letter, with all letters except Q being used. The numbers within each series originally began at 0000001 and ended at 10000000, so that each series consisted of 10,000,000 notes. About 1968 the numbering was altered to begin at 0000000 and end at 9999999, the zero note being removed and destroyed.

The lower letter, or denominational letter, was used for only one specific denomination. For each denominational letter, twenty-five series letters could be used, so that a denominational letter could be used for up to 250,000,000 notes. Nevertheless, the issue was so extensive that every possible denominational letter except Q was eventually used.

When the 1954 issue was being designed it was proposed that the check letters A, B, C and D be restored so that one series of ten million sheet numbers would comprise forty million notes. The effect would have been the more economical use of prefix letters and thus a delay in the exhaustion of possible prefix letter combinations. However the suggestion narrowly missed being acted upon and no check letters were used.

The 1954 "Devil's Face" notes were printed in sheets of 24. The modified protrait notes introduced in 1956 were printed in sheets of 32 until 1968 when the printing of sheets of 40 began. In all cases the notes were "skip-numbered" as in 1937, so that the sheets when stacked could be cut into bricks of consecutively-numbered notes.

Some variation has been reported in the size of numbers on $1, $2 and $10 notes printed by the British American Bank Note Company. This change in the size and style of the numbering head type apparently corresponds closely with the changeover to engraved signatures in 1968.

SIGNATURES OF 1954 NOTES

Before 1968, notes were delivered unsigned by the bank note companies to the Bank of Canada. The signtures were then applied by letterpress by Bank of Canada employees. Because they were printed in a separate process, the signtures show some variation in position. In 1968 the signatures began to be engraved on the face plates starting with the lower denominations so that the notes were printed fully signed. Naturally there can be no variation in the positions of the signtures on these notes. The changeover to engraved signtures is believed to have occurred within the following series:

> $1 CBN Series X/O; $1 BABN Series N/P; $2 Series C/U;
> $5 Series Y/S; S10 Series D/V; $20 Series B/W;
> $50 Series B/H; $100 Series B/J; $1000 Series A/K.

Signatures of the following Bank of Canada officials occur on notes of the 1954 issue:

Senior Deputy Governor	Term of Office
James E. Coyne	Jan. 1, 1950 to Dec. 31, 1954
John Robert Beattie	Jan. 1, 1955 to Dec. 31, 1971
Gerald K. Bouey	Jan. 1, 1972 to Feb. 1, 1973
R. William Lawson	Mar. 1, 1973 to Feb. 29, 1984

Governor	Term of Office
Graham F. Towers	Sept. 10, 1934 to Sept. 10, 1954
James E. Coyne	Jan. 1, 1955 to July 24, 1961
Louis Rasminsky	July 24, 1961 to Feb. 1, 1973
Gerald K. Bouey	Feb. 1, 1973 to Jan. 31, 1987

There are five signature combinations which occur on the 1954 issue. The Coyne-Towers signature combination appears only on the "Devil's Face" notes while the Beattie-Coyne signatures occur on both "Devil's Face" and modified portrait notes. Later combinations are Beattie-Rasminsky, Bouey-Rasminsky and Lawson-Bouey. For denominations of $5 and up, some of the later signature combinations were not always printed.

IMPRINTS OF 1954 NOTES

Both the Canadian Bank Note Company and the British American Bank Note Company participated in the printing of the 1954 issue of notes. At the outset each printer had the contract for the same denominations as for the 1935 and 1937 issues; namely, the British American Bank Note Company printed $2, $5 and $10 while the Canadian Bank Note Company printed the others. In 1959 the Canadian Bank Note Company assumed all further production of the $5 denominations while the British American Bank Note Company shared in the printing of the $1 notes. In the case of the $1 notes, different denominational prefix letters were assigned to each printer. The imprints of the bank note companies are found at the bottom centre of the notes.

1954 ASTERISK NOTES

Prior to the 1954 issue, identical notes were made up to replace notes which were spoiled by the bank note companies during printing or by Bank of Canada employees during signing. Parcels containing defective notes had to be set aside in the Bank's examining room until replacement notes were received from the printer. Because of this delay, and the nuisance of having to supply individually numbered notes to match those which had been spoiled, a new scheme was devised in 1953 for the issue then in preparation. Independently numbered replacement notes were printed with an asterisk preceding the serial number, and stocks of these were maintained to replace defective notes. No asterisk notes were printed for the $50, $100 or $1000 denominations.

It is believed that the asterisk notes were block-numbered. That is, they were not numbered continuously but in blocks with serial number gaps in between, the numbering of each block beginning at some arbitrarily chosen point.

When the two bank note companies began sharing the production of $1 notes in 1959, the asterisk notes were made interchangeable. A $1 BABN asterisk note could be used to replace a defective note in a CBN bundle, and vice-versa.

EXPERIMENTAL ISSUES

In the 1960's and early 1970's mysterious batches of $2 notes with a prefix S/R were released for circulation. These were experimental notes circulated for testing purposes. The S/R $2 numbered from about 1600000 to 2400000 were signed Beattie-Rasminsky, as were the $2 notes in all of the other series within the R group. The next lot, numbered from 2400001 to 26999999 were signed Bouey-Rasminsky, and the last lot, from 2700000 to 2999999 were signed Lawson-Bouey. There the S/R series ended, rather than after the usual ten million notes.

ANOMALIES OF THE 1954 ISSUE

The 1954 issue was more extensive and complicated than any previous emission of the Bank of Canada. A number of intriguing problems arose.

One such problem is the asterisk notes with a denominational letter belonging to a different denomination. A *V/V $1 is known, but the lower V was assigned for use on $10 notes. Similarly, *Z/Z $2 notes are known, but the lower Z letter was supposed to be reserved for $1 notes only. Both of these curiosities may be the result of mistakes made by the Bank of Canada or Bank Note company when numbering the asterisk notes.

Checklist of Prefix Letters for 1954 Devil's Face Issues

Cat.No.	Denom.	Signatures	Printer	Denom. Letter	Series Letters
BC-29a	$1	Coyne-Towers	CBN	A	A B C D E F G H
BC-29aA	$1	Coyne-Towers	CBN	A	A
BC-29b	$1	Beattie-Coyne	CBN	A	H I J K L M N O P R S T
BC-29bA	$1	Beattie-Coyne	CBN	A	A
BC-30a	$2	Coyne-Towers	BABN	B	A B C D
BC-30aA	$2	Coyne-Towers	BABN	B	A
BC-30b	$2	Beattie-Coyne	BABN	B	D E F G H I
BC-30bA	$2	Beattie-Coyne	BABN	B	A
BC-31a A B C	$5	Coyne-Towers	BABN	C	
BC-31aA	$5	Coyne-Towers	BABN	C	A
BC-31b	$5	Beattie-Coyne	BABN	C	C D E F G H I
BC-31bA	$5	Beattie-Coyne	BABN	C	A
BC-32a	$10	Coyne-Towers	BABN	D	A B C D E
BC-32aA	$10	Coyne-Towers	BABN	D	A
BC-32b	$10	Beattie-Coyne	BABN	D	E F G H I J
BC-32bA	$10	Beattie-Coyne	BABN	D	A
BC-33a	$20	Coyne-Towers	CBN	E	A B
BC-33aA	$20	Coyne-Towers	CBN	E	A
BC-33b	$20	Beattie-Coyne	CBN	E	B C D E
BC-33bA	$20	Beattie-Coyne	CBN	E	A
BC-34a	$50	Coyne-Towers	CBN	H	A
BC-34b	$50	Beattie-Coyne	CBN	H	A
BC-35a	$100	Coyne-Towers	CBN	J	A
BC-35b	$100	Beattie-Coyne	CBN	J	A
BC-36	$1000	Coyne-Towers	CBN	K	A

A: = Asterisk replacement note

188

Summary of Technical Details for 1954 Devil's Face Issue

Cat.No.	Denom.	Variety	Printer	Prefixes	Numbers	Qty. Printed
BC-29a	$1	Coyne-Towers	CBN	A/A-G/A	0000001-10000000	70,000,000
BC-29a	$1	Coyne-Towers	CBN	H/A	0000001- 7200000	7,200,000
BC-29aA	$1	Coyne-Towers	CBN	A/A	Unknown Unknown	14,000 (est)
BC-29b	$1	Beattie-Coyne	CBN	H/A	7200001-10000000	2,800,000
BC-29b	$1	Beattie-Coyne	CBN	I/A-S/A	0000001-10000000	100,000,000
BC-29b	$1	Beattie-Coyne	CBN	T/A	0000001-3940000	3,940,000
BC-29bA	$1	Beattie-Coyne	CBN	A/A	Unknown Unknown	8,000 (est)
BC-30a	$2	Coyne-Towers	BABN	A/B-C/B	0000001-10000000	30,000,000
BC-30a	$2	Coyne-Towers	BABN	D/B	0000001-7200000	7,200,000
BC-30aA	$2	Coyne-Towers	BABN	A/B	Unknown Unknown	4,000 (est)
BC-30b	$2	Beattie-Coyne	BABN	D/B	7200001-10000000	2,800,000
BC-30b	$2	Beattie-Coyne	BABN	E/B-H/B	0000001-10000000	40,000,000
BC-30b	$2	Beattie-Coyne	BABN	I/B	0000001-8600000	8,600,000
BC-30bA	$2	Beattie-Coyne	BABN	A/B	Unknown Unknown	5,000 (est)
BC-31a	$5	Coyne-Towers	BABN	A/C-B/C	0000001-10000000	20,000,000
BC-31a	$5	Coyne-Towers	BABN	C/C	0000001-7600000	7,600,000
BC-31aA	$5	Coyne-Towers	BABN	A/C	Unknown Unknown	2,000 (est)
BC-31b	$5	Beattie-Coyne	BABN	C/C	7600001-10000000	2,400,000
BC-31b	$5	Beattie-Coyne	BABN	D/C-H/C	0000001-10000000	50,000,000
BC-31b	$5	Beattie-Coyne	BABN	I/C	0000001-9000000	9,000,000
BC-31bA	$5	Beattie-Coyne	BABN	A/C	Unknown Unknown	5,000 (est)
BC-32a	$10	Coyne-Towers	BABN	A/D-D/D	0000001-10000000	40,000,000
BC-32a	$10	Coyne-Towers	BABN	E/D	0000001-7200000	7,200,000
BC-32aA	$10	Coyne-Towers	BABN	A/D	Unknown Unknown	4,000 (est)
BC-32b	$10	Beattie-Coyne	BABN	E/D	7200001-10000000	2,800,000
BC-32b	$10	Beattie-Coyne	BABN	F/D-I/D	0000001-10000000	40,000,000
BC-32b	$10	Beattie-Coyne	BABN	J/D	0000001-7800000	7,800,000
BC-32bA	$10	Beattie-Coyne	BABN	A/D	Unknown Unknown	4,000 (est)
BC-33a	$20	Coyne-Towers	CBN	A/E	0000001-10000000	10,000,000
BC-33a	$20	Coyne-Towers	CBN	B/E	0000001-6600000	6,600,000
BC-33aA	$20	Coyne-Towers	CBN	A/E	Unknown Unknown	2,000 (est)
BC-33b	$20	Beattie-Coyne	CBN	B/E	6600001-10000000	3,400,000
BC-33b	$20	Beattie-Coyne	CBN	C/E-D/E	0000001-10000000	20,000,000
BC-33b	$20	Beattie-Coyne	CBN	E/E	0000001-2400000	2,400,000
BC-33bA	$20	Beattie-Coyne	CBN	A/E	Unknown Unknown	2,000 (est)
BC-34a	$50	Coyne-Towers	CBN	A/H	0000001-1440000	1,440,000
BC-34b	$50	Beattie-Coyne	CBN	A/H	1440001-4512000	3,072,000
BC-35a	$100	Coyne-Towers	CBN	A/J	0000001-Unknown	Unknown
BC-35b	$100	Beattie-Coyne	CBN	A/J	Unknown-2036000	Unknown
BC-36	$1000	Coyne-Towers	CBN	A/K	0000001-0030000	30,000

A = Asterisk Replacement Note

$1 Issue — 1954

"DEVIL'S FACE" PORTRAIT

BC-29a

Face Design: —/—/Queen Elizabeth II
Colour: Black with green tint

BC-29a

Back Design: —/Western prairie and sky/—
Colour: Green

Issue Date: Engraved: 1954

Imprint: Canadian Bank Note Company Limited

Signatures

Left: Typed J.E. Coyne
Typed J.R. Beattie

Right: Typed G.F. Towers
Typed J.E. Coyne

Cat. No.	Denom.	Variety	VG	F	VF	EF	AU	Unc
BC-29a	$1	Coyne-Towers	4.	6.	8.	12.	17.	25.
BC-29aA	$1	Coyne-Towers	300.	400.	500.	725.	1,100.	1,600.
BC-29b	$1	Beattie-Coyne	3.	5.	6.	9.	13.	20.
BC-29bA	$1	Beattie-Coyne	225.	280.	350.	550.	850.	1,300.

A: = Asterisk replacement note

$2 Issue — 1954

"DEVIL'S FACE" PORTRAIT

BC-30b

Face Design: —/—/Queen Elizabeth II
Colour: Black with red-brown tint

BC-30b

Back Design: —/a country valley in Central Canada/—
Colour: Red-brown

Issue Date: Engraved: 1954

Imprint: British American Bank
Note Company Limited

Signatures

Left: Typed J.E. Coyne
Typed J.R. Beattie

Right: Typed G.F. Towers
Typed J.E. Coyne

Cat. No.	Denom.	Variety	VG	F	VF	EF	AU	Unc
BC-30a	$2	Coyne-Towers	3.	5.	10.	15.	18.	35.
BC-30aA	$2	Coyne-Towers	350.	450.	600.	900.	1,350.	2,000.
BC-30b	$2	Beattie-Coyne	3.	4.	5.	7.	12.	25.
BC-30bA	$2	Beattie-Coyne	320.	400.	500.	750.	1,150.	1,700.

A: = Asterisk replacement note

$5 Issue — 1954

"DEVIL'S FACE" PORTRAIT

BC-31b

Face Design: —/—/Queen Elizabeth II
Colour: Black with blue tint

BC-31b

Back Design: —/Northern stream and forest/—
Colour: Blue

Issue Date: Engraved: 1954

Imprint: British American Bank
Note Company Limited

Signatures

Left: Typed J.E. Coyne
Typed J.R. Beattie

Right: Typed G.F. Towers
Typed J.E. Coyne

Cat. No.	Denom.	Variety	VG	F	VF	EF	AU	Unc
BC-31a	$5	Coyne-Towers	7.	9.	15.	25.	45.	90.
BC-31aA	$5	Coyne-Towers	1,000.	1,500.	2,250.	3,375.	5,000.	7,500.
BC-31b	$5	Beattie-Coyne	7.	9.	13.	20.	35.	70.
BC-31bA	$5	Beattie-Coyne	500.	750.	1,125.	1,700.	2,500.	3,750.

A: = Asterisk replacement note

$10 Issue — 1954

"DEVIL'S FACE" PORTRAIT

BC-32a

Face Design: —/—/Queen Elizabeth II
Colour: Black with purple tint

BC-32a

Back Design: —/Rocky Mountain peak/—
Colour: Purple

Issue Date: Engraved: 1954

Imprint: British American Bank
Note Company Limited

Signatures

Left: Typed J.E. Coyne
Typed J.R. Beattie

Right: Typed G.F. Towers
Typed J.E. Coyne

Cat. No.	Denom.	Variety	VG	F	VF	EF	AU	Unc
BC-32a	$10	Coyne-Towers	10.	12.	15.	25.	45.	90.
BC-32aA	$10	Coyne-Towers	500.	625.	775.	1,175.	1,750.	2,650.
BC-32b	$10	Beattie-Coyne	10.	12.	15.	25.	45.	90.
BC-32bA	$10	Beattie-Coyne	350.	435.	550.	825.	1,225.	1,850.

A: = Asterisk replacement note

$20 Issue — 1954

"DEVIL'S FACE" PORTRAIT

BC-33aA

Face Design: —/—/Queen Elizabeth II
Colour: Black with olive green tint

BC-33aA

Back Design: —/Laurentians in winter/—
Colour: Olive green

Issue Date: Engraved: 1954

Imprint: Canadian Bank Note
Company Limited

Signatures

Left: Typed J.E. Coyne
Typed J.R. Beattie

Right: Typed G.F. Towers
Typed J.E. Coyne

Cat. No.	Denom.	Variety	VG	F	VF	EF	AU	Unc
BC-33a	$20	Coyne-Towers	20.	22.	25.	40.	80.	160.
BC-33aA	$20	Coyne-Towers	500.	750.	1,125.	1,700.	2,500.	3,750.
BC-33b	$20	Beattie-Coyne	20.	22.	24.	35.	70.	140.
BC-33bA	$20	Beattie-Coyne	400.	600.	900.	1,350.	2,100.	3,150.

A: = Asterisk replacement note

$50 Issue — 1954

"DEVIL'S FACE" PORTRAIT

BC-34a

Face Design: —/—/Queen Elizabeth II
Colour: Black with olive green tint

BC-34a

Back Design: —/Atlantic seashore/—
Colour: Orange

Issue Date: Engraved: 1954

Imprint: Canadian Bank Note
Company Limited

Signatures

Left: Typed J.E. Coyne
Typed J.R. Beattie

Right: Typed G.F. Towers
Typed J.E. Coyne

Cat. No.	Denom.	Variety	F	VF	EF	AU	Unc
BC-34a	$50	Coyne-Towers	50.	65.	75.	95.	140.
BC-34b	$50	Beattie-Coyne	50.	63.	70.	90.	130.

"DEVIL'S FACE" PORTRAIT

BC-35a

Face Design: —/—/Queen Elizabeth II
Colour: Black with brown tint

BC-35a

Back Design: —mountain valley and lake/—
Colour: Brown

Issue Date: Engraved: 1954

Imprint: Canadian Bank Note
Company Limited

Signatures

Left: Typed J.E. Coyne
Typed J.R. Beattie

Right: Typed G.F. Towers
Typed J.E. Coyne

Cat. No.	Denom.	Variety	F	VF	EF	AU	Unc
BC-35a	$100	Coyne-Towers	100.	100.	125.	150.	200.
BC-35b	$100	Beattie-Coyne	100.	125.	150.	200.	300.

$1000 Issue — 1954

"DEVIL'S FACE" PORTRAIT

BC-36

Back Design: —/—/Queen Elizabeth II
Colour: Black with rose pink tint

BC-36

Back Design: —/village with lake and hills in Central Canada/—
Colour: Rose pink

Issue Date: Engraved: 1954

Imprint: Canadian Bank Note Company Limited

Signatures

Left: Typed J.E. Coyne

Right: Typed G.F. Towers

Cat. No.	Denom.	Variety	F	VF	EF	AU	Unc
BC-36	$1000	Coyne-Towers	1,000.	1,000.	1,200.	1,350.	1,500.

Checklist of Prefix Letters for 1954 Modified Portrait Issues

Cat.No.	Denom.	Signature	Printer	Letter	Series Letter
BC-37a	$1	Beattie-Coyne	CBN	A	T U V W X Y Z
BC-37a	$1	Beattie-Coyne	CBN	L	A B C D E F G H I J K L M N O P R S T U V W X Y Z
BC-37a	$1	Beattie-Coyne	CBN	N	A B C D E F
BC-37aA	$1	Beattie-Coyne	CBN	A	A
BC-37a-i	$1	Beattie-Coyne	BABN	M	A B C D E F G H
BC-37b	$1	Beattie-Rasminsky	CBN	N	F G H I J K L M N O P R S T U V W X Y Z
BC-37b	$1	Beattie-Rasminsky	CBN	O	A B C D E F G H I J K L S T U V W X Y Z
BC-37b	$1	Beattie-Rasminsky	CBN	Y	A B C D E F G H I J K L M N O P R S T U
BC-37bA	$1	Beattie-Rasminsky	CBN	A	A
BC-37bA	$1	Beattie-Rasminsky	CBN	O	D I S
BC-37bA	$1	Beattie-Rasminsky	CBN	Y	A H M N O
BC-37b-i	$1	Beattie-Rasminsky	BABN	M	H I J K L M N O P R S T U V W X Y Z
BC-37b-i	$1	Beattie-Rasminsky	BABN	P	A B C D E F M N O P R S T U V W X Y Z
BC-37b-i	$1	Beattie-Rasminsky	BABN	Z	A B C D E F G H I J K L M N O P R S T U V W X Y Z
BC-37b-i	$1	Beattie-Rasminsky	BABN	F	A B C D E F G H
BC-37bA-i	$1	Beattie-Rasminsky	BABN	M	A B
BC-37bA-i	$1	Beattie-Rasminsky	BABN	F	A
BC-37c	$1	Bouey-Rasminsky	BABN	F	H I J K L M N O P R S T U V
BC-37cA	$1	Bouey-Rasminsky	BABN	F	C H
BC-37cA	$1	Bouey-Rasminsky	BABN	V	V
BC-37d	$1	Lawson-Bouey	BABN	F	V W X Y Z
BC-37d	$1	Lawson-Bouey	BABN	I	A B C D E
BC-37dA	$1	Lawson-Bouey	BABN	F	X
BC-37dA	$1	Lawson-Bouey	BABN	I	E
BC-38a	$2	Beattie-Coyne	BABN	B	I J K L M N O P R S T U V W X Y Z
BC-38a	$2	Beattie-Coyne	BABN	R	A
BC-38aA	$2	Beattie-Coyne	BABN	B	A
BC-38b	$2	Beattie-Rasminsky	BABN	R	A B C D E F G H I J K L M N O P R S T U V W X Y Z
BC-38b	$2	Beattie-Rasminsky	BABN	U	A B C D E F G H I J K L M N O P R S T U
BC-38bT	$2	Beattie-Rasminsky	BABN	S	R (Test note)
BC-38b	$2	Beattie-Rasminsky	BABN	G	A
BC-38bA	$2	Beattie-Rasminsky	BABN	B	A B
BC-38bA	$2	Beattie-Rasminsky	BABN	R	R
BC-38c	$2	Bouey-Rasminsky	BABN	G	A B C D E F G H I J K L
BC-38cT	$2	Bouey-Rasminsky	BABN	S	R (Test note)
BC-38cA	$2	Bouey-Rasminsky	BABN	G	A
BC-38cA	$2	Bouey-Rasminsky	BABN	Z	Z
BC-38d	$2	Lawson-Bouey	BABN	G	L M N O P R S T U V
BC-38dT	$2	Lawson-Bouey	BABN	S	R (Test note)
BC-38dA	$2	Lawson-Bouey	BABN	G	K O

Checklist of Prefix Letters for 1954 Modified Portrait Issues (Cont'd)

Cat.No.	Denom.	Signature	Printer	Letter	Series Letter
BC-39a	$5	Beattie-Coyne	BABN	C	I J K L M N O P R
BC-39aA	$5	Beattie-Coyne	BABN	C	A
BC-39a-i	$5	Beattie-Coyne	CBN	C	R S T U V W X Y
BC-39aA-i	$5	Beattie-Coyne	CBN	C	R
BC-39b	$5	Beattie-Rasminsky	CBN	C	Y Z
BC-39b	$5	Beattie-Rasminsky	CBN	S	A B C D E F G H I J K L M N O P R S T U V W X Y Z
BC-39b	$5	Beattie-Rasminsky	CBN	X	A B C D E F G H I J K L M N O P R
BC-39bA	$5	Beattie-Rasminsky	CBN	C	R
BC-39bA	$5	Beattie-Rasminsky	CBN	S	L N S V W
BC-39bA	$5	Beattie-Rasminsky	CBN	X	I N R
BC-39c	$5	Bouey-Rasminsky	CBN	X	R S T U V
BC-39cA	$5	Bouey-Rasminsky	CBN	X	R
BC-40a	$10	Beattie-Coyne	BABN	D	J K L M N O P R S T U V W X Y Z
BC-40a	$10	Beattie-Coyne	BABN	T	A B C D E
BC-40aA	$10	Beattie-Coyne	BABN	D	A
BC-40b	$10	Beattie-Rasminsky	BABN	T	E F G H I J K L M N O P R S T U V W X Y Z
BC-40b	$10	Beattie-Rasminsky	BABN	V	A B C D E F G H I J K L M N O P R S T
BC-40bA	$10	Beattie-Rasminsky	BABN	D	A B
BC-40bA	$10	Beattie-Rasminsky	BABN	V	B
BC-41a	$20	Beattie-Coyne	CBN	E	E F G H I J K L M
BC-41aA	$20	Beattie-Coyne	CBN	E	A
BC-41b	$20	Beattie-Rasminsky	CBN	E	M N O P R S T U V W X Y Z
BC-41b	$20	Beattie-Rasminsky	CBN	W	A B C D E F G
BC-41bA	$20	Beattie-Rasminsky	CBN	E	A V
BC-42a	$50	Beattie-Coyne	CBN	H	A
BC-42b	$50	Beattie-Rasminsky	CBN	H	A B
BC-42c	$50	Lawson-Bouey	CBN	H	B C
BC-43a	$100	Beattie-Coyne	CBN	J	A
BC-43b	$100	Beattie-Rasminsky	CBN	J	A B
BC-43c	$100	Lawson-Bouey	CBN	J	B C
BC-44a	$1000	Beattie-Coyne	CBN	K	A
BC-44b	$1000	Beattie-Rasminsky	CBN	K	A
BC-44c	$1000	Bouey-Rasminsky	CBN	K	A
BC-44d	$1000	Lawson-Bouey	CBN	K	A

Summary of Technical Details for 1954 Modified Portrait Issues

Cat.No.	Denom.	Variety	Printer	Prefixes	Numbers	Qty. Printed
BC-37a	$1	Beattie-Coyne	CBN	T/A	3940001-10000000	6,060,000
BC-37a	$1	Beattie-Coyne	CBN	U/A-Z/A	0000001-10000000	60,000,000
BC-37a	$1	Beattie-Coyne	CBN	A/L-Z/A	0000001-10000000	250,000,000
BC-37a	$1	Beattie-Coyne	CBN	A/N-E/N	0000001-10000000	50,000,000
BC-37a	$1	Beattie-Coyne	CBN	F/N	0000001- 5920000	5,920,000
BC-37aA	$1	Beattie-Coyne	CBN	A/A	Unknown Unknown	60,000 (est)
BC-37a-i	$1	Beattie-Coyne	BABN	A/M-G-M	0000001-10000000	70,000,000
BC-37a-i	$1	Beattie-Coyne	BABN	H/M	0000001- 6848000	6,848,000
BC-37b	$1	Beattie-Rasminsky	CBN	F/N	5920001-10000000	4,080,000
BC-37b	$1	Beattie-Rasminsky	CBN	G/N-Z/N	0000001-10000000	190,000,000
BC-37b	$1	Beattie-Rasminsky	CBN	A/0-K/O	0000001-10000000	110,000,000
BC-37b	$1	Beattie-Rasminsky	CBN	L/0	0000001- 7000000	7,000,000
BC-37b	$1	Beattie-Rasminsky	CBN	S/O	7900001-10000000	2,100,000
BC-37b	$1	Beattie-Rasminsky	CBN	T/O	0000001-10000000	10,000,000
BC-37b	$1	Beattie-Rasminsky	CBN	U/O-Z/O	0000000- 9999999	60,000,000
BC-37b	$1	Beattie-Rasminsky	CBN	A/Y-T/Y	0000000- 9999999	190,000,000
BC-37b	$1	Beattie-Rasminsky	CBN	U/Y	0000000- 6439999	6,440,000
BC-37bA	$1	Beattie-Rasminsky	CBN	A/A	Unknown Unknown	400,000 (est)
				D/O	Unknown Unknown	100,000 (est)
				I/O	Unknown Unknown	700,000 (est)
				S/O	Unknown Unknown	400,000 (est)
				A/Y	Unknown Unknown	400,000 (est)
				H/Y	Unknown Unknown	400,000 (est)
				M/Y	Unknown Unknown	400,000 (est)
				N/Y	Unknown Unknown	100,000 (est)
				O/Y	Unknown Unknown	200,000 (est)
BC-37b-i	$1	Beattie-Rasminsky	BABN	H/M	6848001-10000000	3,152,000
BC-37b-i	$1	Beattie-Rasminsky	BABN	I/M-Z/M	0000001-10000000	170,000,000
BC-37b-i	$1	Beattie-Rasminsky	BABN	A/P-E/P	0000001-10000000	50,000,000
BC-37b-i	$1	Beattie-Rasminsky	BABN	F/P	0000001- 7160000	7,160,000
BC-37b-i	$1	Beattie-Rasminsky	BABN	M/P	2720001-10000000	7,280,000
BC-37b-i	$1	Beattie-Rasminsky	BABN	N/P	0000001-10000000	10,000,000
BC-37b-i	$1	Beattie-Rasminsky	BABN	O/P-Z/P	0000000- 9999999	110,000,000
BC-37b-i	$1	Beattie-Rasminsky	BABN	A/Z-Z/Z	0000000- 9999999	250,000,000
BC-37b-i	$1	Beattie-Rasminsky	BABN	A/F-G/F	0000000- 9999999	70,000,000
BC-37b-i	$1	Beattie-Rasminsky	BABN	H/F	0000000- 7239999	7,240,000
BC-37bA-i	$1	Beattie-Rasminsky	BABN	A/M	Unknown Unknown	8,000 (est)
BC-37bA-i	$1	Beattie-Rasminsky	BABN	B/M	Unknown Unknown	3,700,000 (est)
BC-37bA-i	$1	Beattie-Rasminsky	BABN	A/F	Unknown Unknown	400,000 (est)
BC-37c	$1	Bouey-Rasminsky	BABN	H/F	7240000- 9999999	2,260,000
BC-37c	$1	Bouey-Rasminsky	BABN	I/F-U/F	0000000- 9999999	120,000,00
BC-37c	$1	Bouey-Rasminsky	BABN	V/F	0000000- 8559999	8,560,00
BC-37cA	$1	Bouey-Rasminsky	BABN	C/F	Unknown Unknown	400,000 (est)
BC-37cA	$1	Bouey-Rasminsky	BABN	H/F	Unknown Unknown	40,000 (est)
BC-37cA	$1	Bouey-Rasminsky	BABN	V/V	Unknown Unknown	only 2 known
BC-37d	$1	Lawson-Bouey	BABN	V/F	8560000- 9999999	1,440,000
BC-37d	$1	Lawson-Bouey	BABN	W/F-Z/F	0000000- 9999999	40,000,000
BC-37d	$1	Lawson-Bouey	BABN	A/I-D/I	0000000- 9999999	40,000,000
BC-37d	$1	Lawson-Bouey	BABN	E/I	0000000- 4119999	4,120,000
BC-37dA	$1	Lawson-Bouey	BABN	X/F	Unknown Unknown	400,000 (est)
BC-37dA	$1	Lawson-Bouey	BABN	C/I	Unknown Unknown	Unknown

Summary of Technical Details for 1954 Modified Portrait Issues (Cont'd.)

Cat.No.	Denom.	Variety	Printer	Prefixes	Numbers	Qty. Printed
BC-38a	$2	Beattie-Coyne	BABN	I/B	8600001-10000000	1,400,000
BC-38a	$2	Beattie-Coyne	BABN	J/B-Z/B	0000001-10000000	160,000,000
BC-38a	$2	Beattie-Coyne	BABN	A/R	0000001- 5952000	5,952,000
BC-38aA	$2	Beattie-Coyne	BABN	A/B	Unknown Unknown	24,000 (est)
BC-38b	$2	Beattie-Rasminsky	BABN	A/R	5952001-10000000	4,048,000
BC-38b	$2	Beattie-Rasminsky	BABN	B/R-R/R	0000001-10000000	160,000,000
BC-38bT	$2	Beattie-Rasminsky	BABN	S/R	500000-2400000	2,000,000 (est)
BC-38b	$2	Beattie-Rasminsky	BABN	T/R-Z/R	0000001-10000000	70,000,000
BC-38b	$2	Beattie-Rasminsky	BABN	A/U-D/U	0000001-10000000	40,000,000
BC-38b	$2	Beattie-Rasminsky	BABN	E/U-Z/U	0000000- 9999999	210,000,000
BC-38b	$2	Beattie-Rasminsky	BABN	A/G	0000000- 5119999	5,120,000
BC-38bA	$2	Beattie-Rasminsky	BABN	A/B	Unknown Unknown	200,000 (est)
BC-38bA	$2	Beattie-Rasminsky	BABN	B/B	Unknown Unknown	3,200,000 (est)
BC-38bA	$2	Beattie-Rasminsky	BABN	R/R	Unknown Unknown	50,000 (est)
BC-38c	$2	Bouey-Rasminsky	BABN	A/G	5120000- 9999999	4,880,000
BC-38c	$2	Bouey-Rasminsky	BABN	B/G-K/G	0000000- 9999999	100,000,000
BC-38c	$2	Bouey-Rasminsky	BABN	L/G	0000000- 7959999	7,960,000
BC-38cT	$2	Bouey-Rasminsky	BABN	S/R	2400000- 2699999	299,999
BC-38cA	$2	Bouey-Rasminsky	BABN	A/G	Unknown Unknown	700,000 (est)
BC-38cA	$2	Bouey-Rasminsky	BABN	Z/Z	Unknown Unknown	Unknown
BC-38d	$2	Lawson-Bouey	BABN	L/G	7960000- 9999999	2,040,000
BC-38d	$2	Lawson-Bouey	BABN	M/G-U/G	0000000- 9999999	80,000,000
BC-38d	$2	Lawson-Bouey	BABN	V/G	0000000- 7999999	8,000,000
BC-38dT	$2	Lawson-Bouey	BABN	S/R	2700000- 2999999	300,000
BC-38dA	$2	Lawson-Bouey	BABN	K/G	Unknown Unknown	200,000 (est)
BC-38dA	$2	Lawson-Bouey	BABN	K/G	Unknown Unknown	320,000 (est)
BC-39a	$5	Beattie-Coyne	BABN	I/C	9000001-10000000	1,000,000
BC-39a	$5	Beattie-Coyne	BABN	J/C-P/C	0000001-10000000	70,000,000
BC-39a	$5	Beattie-Coyne	BABN	R/C	0000001-0800000	800,000 (est)
BC-39aA	$5	Beattie-Coyne	BABN	A/C	Unknown Unknown	16,000 (est)
BC-39a-i	$5	Beattie-Coyne	CBN	R/C	0800001-10000000	9,200,000 (est)
BC-39a-i	$5	Beattie-Coyne	CBN	S/C-X/C	0000001-10000000	60,000,000
BC-39a-i	$5	Beattie-Coyne	CBN	Y/C	0000001-8256000	8,256,000
BC-39aA-i	$5	Beattie-Coyne	CBN	R/C	Unknown Unknown	8,000 (est)
BC-39b	$5	Beattie-Rasminsky	CBN	Y/C	8256001-10000000	1,744,000
BC-39b	$5	Beattie-Rasminsky	CBN	Z/C	0000001-10000000	10,000,000
BC-39b	$5	Beattie-Rasminsky	CBN	A/S-Z/S	0000001-10000000	250,000,000
BC-39b	$5	Beattie-Rasminsky	CBN	A/X-P/X	0000000- 9999999	160,000,000
BC-39b	$5	Beattie-Rasminsky	CBN	R/X	0000000- 7083999	7,084,000
BC-39bA	$5	Beattie-Rasminsky	CBN	R/C	Unknown Unknown	150,000 (est)
BC-39bA	$5	Beattie-Rasminsky	CBN	L/S	Unknown Unknown	20,000 (est)
BC-39bA	$5	Beattie-Rasminsky	CBN	N/S	Unknown Unknown	40,000 (est)
BC-39bA	$5	Beattie-Rasminsky	CBN	S/S	Unknown Unknown	400,000 (est)
BC-39bA	$5	Beattie-Rasminsky	CBN	V/S	Unknown Unknown	400,000 (est)
BC-39bA	$5	Beattie-Rasminsky	CBN	W/S	Unknown Unknown	60,000 (est)
BC-39bA	$5	Beattie-Rasminsky	CBN	I/X	Unknown Unknown	100,000 (est)
BC-39bA	$5	Beattie-Rasminsky	CBN	N/X	Unknown Unknown	Unknown

Summary of Technical Details for 1954 Portrait Issues (Cont'd.)

Cat.No.	Denom.	Variety	Printer	Prefixes	Numbers	Qty. Printed
BC-39c	$5	Bouey-Rasminsky	CBN	R/X	7084000- 9999999	2,916,000
BC-39c	$5	Bouey-Rasminsky	CBN	S/X-U/X	0000000- 9999999	30,000,000
BC-39c	$5	Bouey-Rasminsky	CBN	V/X	0000000- 6999999	7,000,000
BC-39cA	$5	Bouey-Rasminsky	CBN	R/X	Unknown Unknown	400,000 (est)
BC-40a	$10	Beattie-Coyne	BABN	J/D	7800001-10000000	2,200,000
BC-40a	$10	Beattie-Coyne	BABN	K/D-Z/D	0000001-10000000	150,000,000
BC-40a	$10	Beattie-Coyne	BABN	A/T-D/T	0000001-10000000	40,000,000
BC-40a	$10	Beattie-Coyne	BABN	E/T	0000001- 4688000	4,688,000
BC-40aA	$10	Beattie-Coyne	BABN	A/D	Unknown Unknown	24,000 (est)
BC-40b	$10	Beattie-Rasminsky	BABN	E/T	4688001-10000000	5,312,000
BC-40b	$10	Beattie-Rasminsky	BABN	F/T-M/T	0000001-10000000	80,000,000
BC-40b	$10	Beattie-Rasminsky	BABN	N/T-Z/T	0000000- 9999999	120,000,000
BC-40b	$10	Beattie-Rasminsky	BABN	A/V-S/V	0000000- 9999999	180,000,000
BC-40b	$10	Beattie-Rasminsky	BABN	T/V	0000000- 1719999	1,720,000
BC-40bA	$10	Beattie-Rasminsky	BABN	A/D	Unknown Unknown	100,000 (est)
BC-40bA	$10	Beattie-Rasminsky	BABN	B/D	Unknown Unknown	2,500,000 (est)
BC-40bA	$10	Beattie-Rasminsky	BABN	B/V	Unknown Unknown	50,000 (est)
BC-41a	$20	Beattie-Coyne	CBN	E/E	2400001-10000000	7,600,000
BC-41a	$20	Beattie-Coyne	CBN	F/E-L/E	0000001-10000000	70,000,000
BC-41a	$20	Beattie-Coyne	CBN	M/E	0000001- 2400000	2,400,000
BC-41aA	$20	Beattie-Coyne	CBN	A/E	Unknown Unknown	15,000 (est)
BC-41b	$20	Beattie-Rasminsky	CBN	M/E	2400001-10000000	7,600,000
BC-41b	$20	Beattie-Rasminsky	CBN	N/E-T/E	0000001-10000000	60,000,000
BC-41b	$20	Beattie-Rasminsky	CBN	U/E-Z/E	0000000- 9999999	60,000,000
BC-41b	$20	Beattie-Rasminsky	CBN	A/W-F/W	0000000- 9999999	60,000,000
BC-41b	$20	Beattie-Rasminsky	CBN	G/W	0000000- 8799999	8,800,000
BC-41bA	$20	Beattie-Rasminsky	CBN	A/E	Unknown Unknown	120,000 (est)
BC-41bA	$20	Beattie-Rasminsky	CBN	V/E	Unknown Unknown	80,000 (est)
BC-42a	$50	Beattie-Coyne	CBN	A/H	45122001- 9492000	4,980,000
BC-42b	$50	Beattie-Rasminsky	CBN	A/H	9492001-10000000	508,000
BC-42b	$50	Beattie-Rasminsky	CBN	B/H	0000001- 8071999	8,071,999
BC-42c	$50	Lawson-Bouey	CBN	B/H	8072000- 9999999	1,928,000
BC-42c	$50	Lawson-Bouey	CBN	C/H	0000000- 2015999	2,016,000
BC-43a	$100	Beattie-Coyne	CBN	A/J	0000000-8308000	Unknown
BC-43b	$100	Beattie-Rasminsky	CBN	A/J	8308001-10000000	1,692,000
BC-43b	$100	Beattie-Rasminsky	CBN	B/J	0000001-8007999	8,007,999
BC-43c	$100	Lawson-Bouey	CBN	B/J	8008000-9999999	1,992,000
BC-43c	$100	Lawson-Bouey	CBN	C/J	0000000-3711999	3,712,000
BC-44a	$1000	Beattie-Coyne	CBN	A/K	0030001-0062000	32,000
BC-44b	$1000	Beattie-Rasminsky	CBN	A/K	0062001-0122400	60,400
BC-44c	$1000	Bouey-Rasminsky	CBN	A/K	0122401-0218000	95,599
BC-44d	$1000	Lawson-Bouey	CBN	A/K	0218001-In Issue	

$1 Issue — 1954

MODIFIED PORTRAIT

BC-37b

Face Design: —/—/Queen Elizabeth II
Colour: Black with green tint

BC-37b

Back Design: —/Western prairie and sky/—
Colour: Green

Issue Dated: Engraved: 1954

Imprint: Canadian Bank Note Company, Limited or British American Bank Note Company Limited

Signatures
The signatures were printed until 1968, then engraved on plates.

Left:	Right:
Typed J.R. Beattie	Typed J.E. Coyne
Typed J.R. Beattie	Typed L. Rasminsky
Engr. J.R. Beattie	Engr. L. Rasminsky
Engr. G.K. Bouey	Engr. L. Rasminsky
Engr. R.W. Lawson	Engr. G.K. Bouey

Cat. No.	Denom.	Variety	Printer	VG	F	VF	EF	AU	Unc
BC-37a	$1	Beattie-Coyne	CBN	1.00	1.00	1.50	2.00	3.00	4.00
BC-37aA	$1	Beattie-Coyne	CBN	2.00	4.00	6.00	10.00	20.00	40.00
BC-37a-i	$1	Beattie-Coyne	BABN	1.00	1.25	1.75	2.50	4.00	7.00
BC-37b	$1	Beattie-Rasminsky	CBN	1.00	1.00	1.50	2.00	3.00	4.00
BC-37bA	$1	Beattie-Rasminsky	CBN	1.00	1.50	2.50	4.00	6.00	10.00
BC-37b-i	$1	Beattie-Rasminsky	BABN	1.00	1.00	1.50	2.00	3.00	4.00
BC-37bA-i	$1	Beattie-Rasminsky	BABN	1.00	1.50	2.50	4.00	7.00	12.00
BC-37c	$1	Bouey-Rasminsky	BABN	1.00	1.25	1.75	2.50	4.00	7.00
BC-37cA	$1	Bouey-Rasminsky	BABN	1.00	1.50	2.50	4.00	7.00	12.00
BC-37d	$1	Lawson-Bouey	BABN	1.00	1.25	1.75	2.50	4.00	7.00
BC-37dA	$1	Lawson-Bouey	BABN	1.00	1.25	1.75	3.00	5.00	9.00

A: = Asterisk replacement note

$2 Issue — 1954

MODIFIED PORTRAIT

BC-38bT

Face Design: —/—/Queen Elizabeth II
Colour: Black with red-brown tint

BC-38bT

Back Design: —/a country valley in Central Canada/—
Colour: Red-brown
Issue Date: Engraved: 1954

Imprint: British American Bank Note Company Limited

Signatures
The signatures were printed until 1968, then engraved on plates.

Left: Typed J.R. Beattie	**Right:** Typed J.E. Coyne
Typed J.R. Beattie	Typed L. Rasminsky
Engr. G.K. Bouey	Engr. L. Rasminsky
Engr. R.W. Lawson	Engr. G.K. Bouey

Cat. No.	Denom.	Variety	VG	F	VF	EF	AU	Unc
BC-38a	$2	Beattie-Coyne	2.	4.	5.	7.	12.	25.
BC-38aA	$2	Beattie-Coyne	16.	20.	25.	40.	55.	85.
BC-38b	$2	Beattie-Rasminsky	2.	2.	2.	3.	5.	7.
BC-38bA	$2	Beattie-Rasminsky	2.	2.	3.	6.	10.	15.
BC-38bT	$2	Beattie-Rasminsky	100.	150.	225.	325.	575.	875.
BC-38c	$2	Bouey-Rasminsky	2.	2.	2.	3.	5.	7.
BC-38cA	$2	Bouey-Rasminsky	2.	2.	2.	4.	7.	10.
BC-38cT	$2	Bouey-Rasminsky	75.	110.	165.	250.	425.	650.
BC-38d	$2	Lawson-Bouey	2.	2.	2.	3.	5.	7.
BC-38dA	$2	Lawson-Bouey	2.	2.	3.	6.	10.	15.
BC-38dT	$2	Lawson-Bouey	75.	110.	165.	250.	425.	650.

A: = Asterisk replacement note

MODIFIED PORTRAIT

BC-39b

Face Design: —/—/Queen Elizabeth II
Colour: Black with blue tint

BC-39b

Back Design: —/Northern stream and forest/—
Colour: Blue

Issue Date: Engraved: 1954

Imprint: British American Bank Note Company, Limited and Canadian Bank Note Company, Limited

Signatures
The signatures were printed until 1968, then engraved on plates.

Left: Typed J.R. Beattie
Typed J.R. Beattie
Engr. J.R. Beattie
Engr. G.K. Bouey

Right: Typed J.E. Coyne
Typed L. Rasminsky
Engr. L. Rasminsky
Engr. L. Rasminsky

Cat. No.	Denom.	Variety	Printer	VG	F	VF	EF	AU	Unc
BC-39a	$5	Beattie-Coyne	BABN	6.	9.	14.	20.	30.	40.
BC-39aA	$5	Beattie-Coyne	BABN	18.	22.	28.	42.	65.	100.
BC-39a-i	$5	Beattie-Coyne	CBN	6.	9.	14.	20.	30.	40.
BC-39aA-i	$5	Beattie-Coyne	CBN	18.	22.	28.	42.	65.	100.
BC-39b	$5	Beattie-Rasminsky	CBN	5.	6.	8.	12.	18.	25.
BC-39bA	$5	Beattie-Rasminsky	CBN	10.	13.	16.	24.	35.	50.
BC-39c	$5	Bouey-Rasminsky	CBN	6.	9.	14.	20.	30.	40.
BC-39cA	$5	Bouey-Rasminsky	CBN	9.	11.	15.	22.	33.	48.

A: = Asterisk replacement note

$10 Issue — 1954

MODIFIED PORTRAIT

BC-40a

Face Design: —/—/Queen Elizabeth II
Colour: Black with purple tint

BC-40a

Back Design: —/Rocky Mountain peak/—
Colour: Purple

Issue Date: Engraved: 1954   **Imprint:** British American Bank
                                                    Note Company Limited

Signatures
The signatures were printed until 1968, then engraved on plates.

Left: Typed J.R. Beattie   **Right:** Typed J.E. Coyne
          Typed J.R. Beattie   Typed L. Rasminsky
          Engr. J.R. Beattie   Engr. L. Rasminsky

Cat. No.	Denom.	Variety	VG	F	VF	EF	AU	Unc
BC-40a	$10	Beattie-Coyne	10.	12.	14.	20.	30.	40.
BC-40aA	$10	Beattie-Coyne	16.	21.	27.	40.	60.	120.
BC-40b	$10	Beattie-Rasminsky	10.	11.	13.	16.	25.	35.
BC-40bA	$10	Beattie-Rasminsky	10.	13.	16.	24.	35.	50.

A: = Asterisk replacement note

$20 Issue — 1954

MODIFIED PORTRAIT

BC-41b

Face Design: —/—/Queen Elizabeth II
Colour: Black with olive green tint

BC-41b

Back Design: —/Laurentians in winter/—
       Colour: Olive green

Issue Date: Engraved: 1954   **Imprint:** Canadian Bank Note
                                                  Company Limited

Signatures
The signatures were printed until 1968, then engraved on plates.
           Left: Typed J.R. Beattie   **Right:** Typed J.E. Coyne
                  Typed J.R. Beattie   Typed L. Rasminsky
                  Engr. J.R. Beattie   Engr. L. Rasminsky

Cat. No.	Denom.	Variety Printer	VG	F	VF	EF	AU	Unc
BC-41a	$20	Beattie-Coyne	22.	27.	32.	40.	50.	75.
BC-41aA	$20	Beattie-Coyne	25.	40.	50.	100.	150.	225.
BC-41b	$20	Beattie-Rasminsky	20.	22.	27.	33.	42.	60.
BC-41bA	$20	Beattie-Rasminsky	23.	28.	35.	70.	135.	200.

A: = Asterisk replacement note

$50 Issue — 1954

MODIFIED PORTRAIT

BC-42a

Face Design: —/—/Queen Elizabeth II
Colour: Black with orange tint

BC-42a

Back Design: —/Atlantic seashore/—
Colour: Orange

Issue Date: Engraved: 1954

Imprint: Canadian Bank Note
Company Limited

Signatures
The signatures were printed until 1968, then engraved on plates.

Left: Typed J.R. Beattie
Typed J.R. Beattie
Engr. J.R. Beattie
Engr. R.W. Lawson

Right: Typed J.E. Coyne
Typed L. Rasminsky
Engr. L. Rasminsky
Engr. G.K. Bouey

Cat. No.	Denom.	Variety Printer	VG	F	VF	EF	AU	Unc
BC-42a	$50	Beattie-Coyne	50.	53.	58.	65.	75.	100.
BC-42b	$50	Beattie-Rasminsky	50.	52.	55.	60.	70.	90.
BC-42c	$50	Lawson-Bouey	75.	90.	110.	165.	250.	375.

$100 Issue — 1954

MODIFIED PORTRAIT

BC-43b

Face Design: —/—/Queen Elizabeth II
Colour: Black with brown tint

BC-43b

Back Design: —/mountain valley and lake/—
Colour: Brown

Issue Date: Engraved: 1954

Imprint: Canadian Bank Note
Company Limited

Signatures
The signatures were printed until 1968, then engraved on plates.

Left: Typed J.R. Beattie
Typed J.R. Beattie
Engr. J.R. Beattie
Engr. R.W. Lawson

Right: Typed J.E. Coyne
Typed L. Rasminsky
Engr. L. Rasminsky
Engr. G.K. Bouey

Cat. No.	Denom.	Variety Printer	VF	EF	AU	Unc
BC-43a	$100	Beattie-Coyne	110.	120.	140.	160.
BC-43b	$100	Beattie-Rasminsky	110.	120.	140.	160.
BC-43c	$100	Lawson-Bouey	110.	120.	140.	160.

Lower grade notes are not collectable and command no premium.

$1000 Issue — 1954

MODIFIED PORTRAIT

BC-44c

Face Design: —/—/Queen Elizabeth II
Colour: Black with rose pink tint

BC-44c

Back Design: —/village with lake and hills in Central Canada
Colour: Rose pink

Issue Date: Engraved: 1954

Imprint: Canadian Bank Note
Company Limited

Signatures
The signatures were printed until 1968, then engraved on plates.

Left:	Right:
Typed J.R. Beattie	Typed J.E. Coyne
Typed J.R. Beattie	Typed L. Rasminsky
Engr. J.R. Beattie	Engr. L. Rasminsky
Engr. G.K. Bouey	Engr. L. Rasminsky
Engr. R.W. Lawson	Engr. G.K. Bouey

Cat. No.	Denom.	Variety Printer	VF	EF	AU	Unc
BC-44a	$1000	Beattie-Coyne	1,000.	1,050.	1,100.	2,100.
BC-44b	$1000	Beattie-Rasminsky	1,000.	1,050.	1,100.	2,100.
BC-44c	$1000	Bouey-Rasminsky	1,000.	1,025.	1,050.	1,100.
BC-44d	$1000	Lawson-Bouey	1,000.	1,000.	1,025.	1,050.

$1 Centennial Issue of 1967

Special $1 notes were issued in 1967 to commemorate the centennial of Confederation. The face of the note resembles that of the 1954 $1 issue, except for the maple leaf centennial symbol at the left and references to the centennial along the top and bottom. The back vignette portrays the original Centre Block of the Parliament buildings, which was destroyed by fire in 1916. The same vignette was used on the face of the 1872 $1000 Dominion note. Restoration of the original die was done by Gordon Yorke. He also re-engraved the sky and added landscaping to both sides of the building and to the foreground.

Deliveries of the 1954 $1 notes to the chartered banks were suspended through 1967, and the commemorative notes were distributed exclusively. A special collector's issue was prepared with the dates 1867 1967 replacing the serial numbers. These notes were available only from the Bank of Canada but soon began to enter circulation. Because they were hoarded by the public, these special notes remain very common, while the regular serial number notes have to a greater extent disappeared.

Both bank note companies were involved in the printing of these notes but their imprints were omitted. The Canadian Bank Note Co. printed the notes in group "O", series L, M, N, O, P, R and S, and the British American Bank Note Co. printed the notes in group "P", series F, G, H, I, J, K, L and M. Because there are no imprints, the notes of the special collector's issue produced by the two companies are not given separate catalogue numbers.

The serial numbers of these notes conform to gaps in the numbering of the 1954 $1 notes which occurred between 1966 and 1968.

Checklist of Prefix Letters for 1967 Issues

Cat.No.	Denom.	Variety	Printer	Denom. Letter	Series Letter
BC-45a	$1	Commemorative Serial No.	CBN	None	None
BC-45a	$1	Commemorative Serial No.	BABN	None	None
BC-45b	$1	Regular Serial No.	CBN	O	L M N O P R S
BC-45bA	$1	Asterisk	CBN	O	L N
BC-45b	$1	Regular Serial No.	BABN	P	F G H I J K L M
BC-45bA	$1	Asterisk	BABN	M	B
BC-45bA	$1	Asterisk	BABN	P	F

A: = Asterisk replacement note

Summary of Technical Details

Cat.No.	Denom.	Variety	Printer	Prefixes	Numbers	Qty. Printed
BC-45a	$1	1867 1967 in place of serial number	CBN or BABN	None	None	12,000,000
BC-45b	$1	Regular serial number	CBN	L/O	7000001-10000000	3,000,000
BC-45b	$1	Regular serial number	CBN	M/O-R/O	0000001-10000000	50,000,000
BC-45b	$1	Regular serial number	CBN	S/O	0000001- 7900000	7,900,000
BC-45bA	$1	Regular serial number	CBN	L/O	Unknown Unknown	40,000 (est)
BC-45bA	$1	Regular serial number	CBN	N/O	Unknown Unknown	175,000 (est)
BC-45b	$1	Regular serial number	BABN	F/P	7160001-10000000	2,840,000
BC-45b	$1	Regular serial number	BABN	G/P-L/P	0000001-10000000	60,000,000
BC-45b	$1	Regular serial number	BABN	M/P	0000001- 2720000	2,720,000
BC-45bA	$1	Regular serial number	BABN	B/M	Unknown Unknown	600,000 (est)
BC-45bA	$1	Regular serial number	BABN	F/P	Unknown Unknown	70,000 (est)

$1 Issue — 1967

BC-45a

Face Design: Centennial symbol/—/Queen Elizabeth II.
The Centennial symbol is a stylized Maple Leaf
divided into eleven triangles.
Colour: Black with green tint

BC-45a

Back Design: —/Old Parliament Buildings/—
Colour: Green

Issue Date: Engraved: 1967   **Imprint:** None
Printer: British American Bank
Note Company or
Canadian Bank Note Co.
Signatures
Left: Engr. J.R. Beattie   **Right:** Engr. L. Rasminsky

Varieties

SPECIAL COMMEMORATIVE NUMBER 1867-1967

REGULAR SERIAL NUMBER WITH NORMAL PREFIX LETTERS AND DIGITS

ASTERISK SERIAL NUMBER

Cat. No.	Variety	F	VF	EF	AU	Unc
BC-45a	No serial number	1.00	1.00	2.00	3.00	4.00
BC-45b	Prefix L/O	1.00	2.00	7.00	11.00	15.00
BC-45b	Prefix M/O, N/O, O/O, P/O, R/O	1.00	1.25	4.00	6.00	8.00
BC-45b	Prefix S/O	1.00	2.00	6.00	9.00	12.00
BC-45b	Prefix F/P	1.00	2.00	7.00	11.00	15.00
BC-45b	Prefix G/P, H/P, I/P, J/P, K/P, L/P	1.00	1.25	4.00	6.00	8.00
BC-45b	Prefix M/P	10.00	20.00	50.00	100.00	150.00
BC-45bA	Prefix B/M	1.50	3.00	6.00	9.00	12.00
BC-45bA	Prefix L/O	1.75	5.00	10.00	15.00	22.00
BC-45bA	Prefix N/O	1.50	3.00	8.00	11.00	15.00
BC-45bA	Prefix F/P	2.50	5.00	10.00	15.00	22.00

Issues of 1969 — 1975

The 1969-1975 issue, unlike the previous Bank of Canada issues, does not have a common date for all denominations. The issue dates span the years 1969 to 1975. Termination of the 1954 issue was necessary for two reasons. Almost all prefix letter combinations had been used up, and counterfeiting was rampant, particularly affecting the intermediate and higher denominations. Advanced security features were incorporated into the new multicolour issue. These have been so successful that there has been to date no counterfeit problem involving the new notes. The $1000 denomination was not included in this issue, and $1000 notes dated 1954 are still being issued.

The traditional promise "will pay to the bearer on demand" was finally replaced by the words "this note is legal tender", reflecting the fact that government paper currency had long since ceased to be redeemable in gold.

George Gundersen engraved the portrait of Queen Elizabeth used on the $1, $2 and $20 notes, as well as the portraits of Sir John A. Macdonald on the $10 and William Lyon Mackenzie King on the $50. He also engraved the Rocky Mountain scene on the back of the $20 note. Gordon Yorke engraved the portraits of Sir Wilfrid Laurier on the $5 and Sir Robert Borden on the $100 note. Yorke also engraved the scenes on the backs of the $2, $5 and $100.

PREFIXES AND NUMBERING

Printing is in sheets of 40, with the notes in the sheet "skip-numbered" in jumps of 1000, so that a stack of 1000 sheets when cut will yield bricks of 1000 consecutively-numbered notes. The serial numbers are in red at the left and in blue at the right.

In a departure from previous practice, the prefix letters are no longer arranged in the form of the fraction. Instead, the denominational letter appears first, followed by the series letter. The series letters may include all letters from "A" to "Z" excepting I, O, and Q because of their resemblance to numerals. Thus any given denominational letter may accommodate twenty-three series, or 230,000,000 notes. Each series is numbered from 0000000 to 9999999, with the zero note being removed and destroyed prior to issue.

With the imminent exhaustion of the possible prefix letter combinations, the triple letter prefix was introduced in 1981. The first letter designates the printer and the next two letters indicate the series. Four initials have been employed to date: A and B for BABN and E and F for CBN. Letter B (also BABN) will be released soon.

LITHOGRAPHED BACKS

In 1984 a change was initiated in the printing technique used for the backs of Bank of Canada notes, from the intaglio steel engraved process to the lithographic process. This cost-cutting measure was begun with the $1 and $2 notes, and gradually extended to included most other denominations. The changeover numbers are:

		Last Note with Engraved Back is:	First Note with Engraved Back is:
$1	BABN	AFF3799999	AFF3800000
$1	BABN Replacement	AAX2159999	AXX2160000
$1	CBN	EAK1199999	EAK1200000
$1	CBN Replacement	EAX0619999	EAX0620000
$2		AGJ9999999	AGK0000000
$2	Replacement	ABX1119999	ABX1120000
$10		EEV4999999	EEV5000000
$10	Replacement	EDX2639999	EDX2640000

SIGNATURES

Signatures of the following Bank of Canada officials occur on notes of the 1969-1975 issues: in all cases the signatures are engraved on the face plates.

Senior Deputy Governor	*Term of Office*
John Robert Beattie	Jan. 1, 1955 to Dec. 31, 1971
Gerald K. Bouey	Jan. 1, 1972 to Feb. 1, 1973
R. William Lawson	March 1, 1973 to Feb. 29, 1984
John W. Crow	March 1, 1984 to Jan. 31, 1987
Gordon G, Thiessen	Oct. 27, 1987 to date

Governor	*Term of Office*
Louis Rasminsky	July 24, 1961 to Feb. 1, 1973
Gerald K. Bouey	Feb. 1, 1973 to Jan. 31, 1987
John W. Crow	Feb. 1, 1987 to date

IMPRINTS

Both the British American and Canadian Bank Note companies have participated in the printing of the multicoloured notes, but there are no imprints. The work of the two companies can be distinguished by the styles of type used in the serial numbers, which show slight differences.

ASTERISK REPLACEMENT NOTES

Replacement of defective notes by asterisk notes was continued when the 1969-1975 issue was introduced. The highest denomination of the 1954 issue to be printed with asterisks was the $20; however, all denominations in the 1969-1975 issue including the $50 and $100 notes occur with asterisks in front of the two letter prefix type.

When the triple letter prefix notes were introduced in 1981, the use of asterisk notes was discontinued. For triple letter prefix notes, a replacement note is designated by the use of an "X" for the third letter.

Asterisk Notes	**"X" Replacement Notes**
BC-46aA	**BC-46A-i**

The rule that the first prefix letter on double prefix notes may only be associated with one specific denomination was violated once in the 1969-1975 issue. The denominational letter "R" was used for both $2 and $5 notes. The RS $2 and $5 notes are believed to be experimental, placed in circulation in limited quantity to test the durability of new innovations in ink or paper composition or some other changes. This prefix corresponds to the mysterious prefix S/R which was used on some experimental $2 notes of the 1954 issue. The $2 with the RS prefix appeared in circulation long before the other $2 notes in the R group. It has been reported that some of the $2 RS notes are of an unusually dark colour.

Experimental issues have also appeared in the triple letter prefix notes. For the $1 (1973 issue) the prefixes AXA and EXA have been used on experimental notes.

$2 Experimental Note
BC-47aT

$5 Experimental Note
BC-48bT

$1 Experimental Note
BC-46aT-i

$1 Experimental Note
BC-46bT-i

Checklist of Prefix Letters for 1969-1975 Issues

Cat.No.	Denom.	Date	Variety	Denom. Letter	Series Letter
BC-46a	$1	1973	Lawson-Bouey; 2 letters	A	A B C D E F G H J K L M N P R S T U V W X Y Z
BC-46aA				A	A B L N (Asterisk note)
BC-46a				F	A B C D E F G H J K L M N P R S T U V W X Y Z
BC-46aA				F	A G H N V (Asterisk note)
BC-46a				G	A B C D E F G H J K L M N P R S T U V W X Y Z
BC-46aA				G	F L U Y (Asterisk note)
BC-46a				I	A B C D E F G H J K L M N P R S T U V W X Y Z
BC-46aA				I	A G L V (Asterisk note)
BC-46a				L	A B C D E F G H J K L M N P R S T U V W X Y Z
BC-46a				M	A B C D E F G H J K L M N P R S T U V W X Y Z
BC46-aA				M	C D M R Z (Asterisk note)
BC-46a				N	A B C D E F G H J K L M N P R S T U V W X Y Z
BC-46aA				N	P (Asterisk note)
BC-46a				O	A D C D E F G H J K L M N P R S T U V
BC-46aA				O	G L (asterisk note)
BC-46a				P	A
BC-46aA-i	$1	1973	Lawson-Bouey; 3 letters (steel engraved back)	AA	A B C D E F G H J K L M N P R S T U V W Y Z
BC-46a-i				AA	X (Replacement note)
BC-46a-i				AC	A B C D E F G H J K L M N P R S T U V W Y Z
BC-46aT-i				AF	A B C D E F
BC-46a-i				AX	A (Test note)
BC-46a-i				EA	A B C D E F G H J K
BC-46a-i	$1	1973	Lawson-Bouey; 3 letter (lithographed back)	AF	F G H J K L M N P R S T U V W Y Z
BC-46a-i				AL	A B C D F G H J K L M
BC-46aA-i				EA	K L M N
bc-46aA-i				AA	X (Replacement note)
BC-46b	$1	1973	Crow-Bouey	EA	N P R S T U V W Y Z
BC-46bA				EA	X (Replacement note)
BC-46b				AL	M N P R S T U V W Y Z
BC-46b				AM	A B C D E F G H J K L M N P R S T U V W Y Z

Checklist of Prefix Letters for 1969-1975 Issues (Cont'd.)

Cat.No.	Denom.	Date	Variety	Denom. Letter	Series Letter
BC-46b	$1	1973	Crow-Bouey	EC	A B C D E F G H J K L M N P
BC-46bT	$1	1973	Crow-Bouey	EX	A (Test note)
BC-46bA	$1	1973	Crow-Bouey	AA	X (Replacement note)
BC-46b				BA	A B C D E F G H J K L M N P R S T U V W Y Z
BC-46B				BC	A B C D E F G H J K L M N P R S T U V W Y Z
BC-46b				BF	A B C D E F G H J K
BC-46bA				BA	X (Replacement Note)
BC-47a	$2	1974	Lawson-Bouey; 2 letters	B	A B C D E F G H J K L M N P R S T U V W X Y Z
BC-47aA				B	A C J M X (Asterisk note)
BC-47a				R	A B C D E F G H J K L M N P R T U V W Y Z
BC-47aA				R	A E W (Asterisk note)
BC-47aT				R	S (Test note)
BC-47a				U	A B C D E F G H J K L M
BC-47aA				U	G (Asterisk note)
BC-47a-i	$2	1974	Lawson-Bouey; 3 letters	AB	B C D E F G H J K L M N P R S T U V W Y Z
				A	A B C D E F G H J
BC-47a-i				AG	X (Replacement note)
BC-47aA-i				AB	K L M N P R S T U V W Y Z
BC-47b	$2	1974	Crow-Bouey	AG	A B C D E
BC-47b				AR	X (Replacement note)
BC-47bA				AB	X (Replacement note)
BC-48a	$5	1972	Bouey-Rasminsky	C	A B C D E F G H J K L M N P
BC-48aA				C	A B D (Asterisk note)
BC-48b	$5	1972	Lawson-Bouey; 2 letters	C	P R S T U V W X Y Z
BC-48bA				C	S U V (Asterisk note)
BC-48bT				R	S (Test note)
BC-48b				X	A
BC-48b	$5	1972	Lawson-Bouey	S	A B C D E F G H J K L M N P R S T U V W X Y Z
BC-48bA				S	B F L P W (Asterisk note)

Checklist of Prefix Letters for 1969-1975 Issues (Cont'd.)

Cat.No.	Denom.	Date	Variety	Denom. Letter	Series Letter
BC-49a	$10	1971	Beattie-Rasminsky	D	A B C D E F G H J K L
BC-49aA				D	A B E G (Asterisk note)
BC-49b	$10	1971	Bouey-Rasminsky	D	L M N P R S T U V W X
BC-49bA				D	K R (Asterisk note)
BC-49c	$10	1971	Lawson-Bouey; 2 letters	D	X Y Z
BC-49cA	$10	1971	Lawson-Bouey; 2 letters	D	Y (Asterisk note)
BC-49c	$10	1971	Lawson-Bouey; 2 letters	T	A B C D E F G H J K L M N P R S T U V W X Y Z
BC-49cA				T	C G L T (Asterisk note)
BC-49c				V	A B C D E F G H J K L M N P R S T U V W X
BC-49cA				V	A J L T (Asterisk note)
BC-49c-i	$10	1971	Lawson-Bouey; 3 letters (steel engraved back)	ED	A B C D E F G H J K L M N P R S T U V W Y Z
BC-49aA-i				ED	X (Replacement note)
BC-49c-i				EE	A B C D E F G H J K L M N P
BC-49c-i	$10	1971	Lawson-Bouey; 3 letters (anomaly)	EE	T
BC-49d	$10	1971	Crow-Bouey (steel engraved back)	EE	P R S T U V
BC-49d	$10	1971	Crow-Bouey (lithographed back)	EE	V W Y Z
BC-49d				ET	A B C D E F G H J K L M N P R S T U V W Y Z
BC-49d				FD	A B C
BC-49dA				ED	X (Replacement note)
BC-49e	$10	1971	Thiessen-Crow	FD	C D E G H J K L M N P R
BC-49eA	$10	1971	Thiessen-Crow	ED	X (Replacement note)
BC-50a	$20	1969	Beattie-Rasminsky	E	A B C D E F G H J K L M N P R S T U V W X Y Z
BC-50aA				E	A B H M V X (Asterisk note)
BC-50b	$20	1969	Lawson-Bouey; 2 letters	E	Z
BC-50bA				E	Z (Asterisk note)
BC-50b				W	A B C D E F G H J K L M N P R S T U V W X Y Z
BC-50bA				W	E F L N V (Asterisk note)

Checklist of Prefix Letters for 1969-1975 Issues (Cont'd.)

Cat.No.	Denom.	Date	Variety	Denom. Letter	Series Letter
BC-50b	$20			Y	A B C D E F G H
BC-50bA		1969	Lawson-Bouey; 2 letters	Y	A (Asterisk note)
BC-51a	$50	1969	Lawson-Bouey; 2 letters	H	A B C D
BC-51aA				H	B C (Asterisk note)
BC-51a-i	$50	1975	Lawson-Bouey; 3 letters	E H	A B C D E F
BC-51aA-i				E H	X (Replacement note)
BC-51b		1975	Crow-Bouey	E H	F G H J K L M
BC-51bA				E H	X (Replacement note)
BC-52a	$100	1975	Lawson-Bouey; 2 letters	J	A B C D
BC-52aA				J	A C (Asterisk note)
BC-52a-i		1975	Lawson-Bouey; 3 letters	A J	A B C
BC-52aA-i				A J	X (Replacement note)
BC-52b		1975	Crow-Bouey	A J	C D E F G H J
BC-52bA				A J	X (Replacement note)

221

Summary of Technical Details

Cat.No.	Denom.	Date	Variety	Prefixes	Numbers	Qty. Printed
BC-46a	$1	1973	Lawson-Bouey; 2 letters	AA-AZ	0000000-9999999	230,000,000
BC-46a				FA-FZ	0000000-9999999	230,000,000
BC-46a				GA-GZ	0000000-9999999	230,000,000
BC-46a				IA-IZ	0000000-9999999	230,000,000
BC-46a				LA-LZ	0000000-9999999	230,000,000
BC-46a				MA-MZ	0000000-9999999	230,000,000
BC-46a				NA-NZ	0000000-9999999	230,000,000
BC-46a				OA-OV	0000000-9999999	190,000,000
BC-46a				PA	0000000-9999999	10,000,000
BC-46aA	$1	1973	Lawson-Bouey; 2 letters (Asterisk note)	AA		1,000,000 est.
BC-46aA				AB		1,000 est.
BC-46aA				AL		500,000 est.
BC-46aA				AN		1,500,000 est.
BC-46aA				FA		700,000 est.
BC-46aA				FG		500,000 est.
BC-46aA				FH		1,000 est.
BC-46aA				FN		400,000 est.
BC-46aA				FV		1,000,000 est.
BC-46aA				GF		400,000 est.
BC-46aA				GL		400,000 est.
BC-46aA				GU		400,000 est.
BC-46aA				GY		400,000 est.
BC-46aA				IA		400,000 est.
BC-46aA				IG		200,000 est.
BC-46aA				IL		500,000 est.
BC-46aA				IV		300,000 est.
BC-46aA				MC		400,000 est.
BC-46aA				MD		1,000 est.
BC-46aA				MM		400,000 est.
BC-46aA				MR		400,000 est.
BC-46aA				MZ		500,000 est.
BC-46aA				NP		400,000 est.
BC-46aA				OG		400,000 est.
BC-46aA				OL		100,000 est.
BC-46a-i	$1	1973	Lawson-Bouey; 3 letters (steel engraved back)	AAA-AAZ	0000000-9999999	220,000,000
BC-46a-i				ACA-ACZ	0000000-9999999	220,000,000
BC-46a-i				AFA-AFZ	0000000-9999999	220,000,000
BC-46a-i				ALA-ALM	0000000-9999999	
BC-46a-i				EAA-EAN	0000000-9999999	
BC-46aA-i	$1	1973	Replacement Note	AAX		3,300,000 est.
BC-46aT-i	$1	1973	Test Note	AXA		1,000,000 est.
BC-46a-i				EAA-EAK		91,200,000
BC-46a-i	$1	1973	Lawson-Bouey; 3 letters (lithographed back)	AFF-AFZ		166,200,000
BC-46a-i				EAK-EAN		37,720,000
BC-46a-i				ALA-ALM	(ALE not seen)	101,400,000
BC-46aA-i	$1	1973	Replacement Note	AAX		Unknown
BC-46aA-i				EAX		Unknown
BC-46b	$1	1973	Crow-Bouey	EAN-EAZ		
BC-46b				ALM-ALZ		108,600,000
BC-46b				AMA-AMZ	0000000-9999999	220,000,000
BC-46b				ECA-ECP		140,000,000

Summary of Technical Details (Cont'd.)

Cat.No.	Denom.	Date	Variety	Prefixes	Numbers	Qty. Printed
BC-46b				BAA-BAZ		220,000,000
BC46b				BCA-BCZ		220,000,000
BC-46b				BFA-BFK		100,000,000
BC-46bA	$1	1973	Replacement Note	AAX		In issue
BC-46bA	$1	1973	Replacement Note	BAX		In issue
BC-46bA				EAX		In issue
BC-46bT				EXA		800,000 est.
						Not issued
BC-47a	$2	1974	Lawson-Bouey; 2 letters	BA-BZ		230,000,000
BC-47a				RA-RZ		230,000,000
BC-47a				UA-UM		119,520,000
BC-47aA	$2	1974	Asterisk Note	BA		500,000 est.
BC-47aA				BC		200,000 est.
BC-47aA				BJ		200,000 est.
BC-47aA				BM		400,000 est.
BC-47aA				BX		200,000 est.
BC-47aA				RA		100,000 est.
BC-47aA				RE		400,000 est.
BC-47aA				RW		400,000 est.
BC-47aA				UG		200,000 est.
BC-47aT	$2	1974	Test Note	RS		Unknown
BC-47a-i	$2	1974	Lawson-Bouey; 3 letters	ABA-ABZ		220,000,000 est.
BC-47a-i				AGA-AGJ		90,000,000 est.
BC-47aA-i	$2	1974	Replacement Note	ABX	0000000-1119999	1,200,000
BC-47b	$2	1974	Crow-Bouey	AGK-AGZ		130,000,000
BC-47b				ARA-ARE		48,800,000 est.
BC-47bA	$2	1974	Replacement Note	ABX	1120000-1559999	440,000 est.
BC-48a	$5	1972	Bouey-Rasminsky	CA-CP		134,200,000
BC-48aA	$5	1972	Asterisk Note	CA		500,000 est.
BC-48aA				CC		400,000 est.
BC-48aA				CD		400,000 est.
BC-48b	$5	1972	Lawson-Bouey; 2 letters	CP-CZ		95,800,000
BC-48b				SA-SZ		230,000,000
BC-48b				XA		5,520,000
BC-48bT	$5	1972	Test Note	RS		
BC-48bA	$5	1972	Asterisk Note	CS		50,000 est.
BC-48bA				CU		200,000 est.
BC-48bA				CV		300,000 est.
BC-48bA				SB		500,000 est.
BC-48bA				SF		400,000 est.
BC-48bA				SL		200,000 est.
BC-48bA				SP		500,000 est.
BC-48bA				SW		200,000 est.
BC-49a	$10	1971	Beattie-Rasminsky	DA-DL		100,800,000
BC-49aA	$10	1971	Asterisk Note	DA		400,000 est.
BC-49aA				DB		400,000 est.
BC-49aA				DE		Unknown
BC-49aA				DG		200,000 est.
BC-49b	$10	1971	Bouey-Rasminsky	DL-DX		99,640,000
BC-49bA				DK		500,000 est.
BC-49cA				DR		300,000 est.

Summary of Technical Details (Cont'd.)

Cat.No.	Denom.	Date	Variety	Prefixes	Numbers	Qty. Printed
BC-49c	$10	1971	Lawson-Bouey; 2 letters	DX-DZ		29,560,000
BC-49c				TA-TZ		230,000,000
BC-49c				VA-VX		207,240,000
BC-49cA	$10	1971	Asterisk Note	DY		500,000 est.
BC-49cA				TC		400,000 est.
BC-49cA				TG		200,000 est.
BC-49cA				TL		400,000 est.
BC-49cA				TT		400,000 est.
BC-49cA				VA		400,000 est.
BC-49cA				VJ		100,000 est.
BC-49cA	$10	1971	Lawson-Bouey; 2 letters	VL		300,000 est.
BC-49cA			Asterisk Note	VT		200,000 est.
BC-49c-i	$10	1971	Lawson-Bouey; 3 letters (steel engraved)	EDA-EDZ	0000000-9999999	220,000,000
BC-49c-i				EEA-EEN	0000000-9999999	130,000,000
BC-49c-i				EEP	0000000-9000000	9,000,000
BC-49cA-i	$10	1971	Replacement Note	EDX		Unknown
BC-49c-i	$10	1971	Lawson-Bouey; 3 letters (lithographed back)	EET	9360001-9999999	640,000 est.
BC-49cA-i	$10	1971	Replacement note	EDX		Unknown
BC-49d	$10	1971	Crow-Bouey (steel engraved)	EEP	9000001-9360000	360,000
BC-49d	$10	1971	Crow-Bouey (steel engraved)	EER-EET		Unknown
BC-49d				EEU-EEV	0000000-9999999	15,000,000
BC-49dA	$10	1971	Replacement Note	EDX	-2639999	Unknown
BC-49d	$10	1971	Crow-Bouey (lithographed back)	EEV-EEZ	0000000-9999999	35,000,000
BC-49d				ETA-ETZ		220,000,000
BC-49d				FDA-FDB	0000000-9999999	20,000,000
BC-49d				FDC	0000000-4799999	4,800,000 est.
BC-49dA	$10	1971	Replacement Note	EDX	2640000-	In issue
BD-49e	$10	1971	Thiessen-Crow	FDC	4800000-9999999	5,200,000 est. In issue
BD-49eA	$10	1971	Replacement Note	EDX		In issue
BC-50a	$20	1969	Beattie-Rasminsky	EA-EZ		224,520,000
BC-50aA	$20	1969	Asterisk Note	EA		500,000 est.
BC-50aA				EB		400,000 est.
BC-50aA				EH		400,000 est.
BC-50aA				EM		400,000 est.
BC-50aA				EV		20,000 est.
BC-50aA				EX		100,000 est.
BC-50b	$20	1969	Lawson-Bouey; 2 letters	EZ	4520000-9999999	5,480,000 est.
BC-50b				WA-WZ		230,000,000
BC-50bA	$20	1969	Asterisk Note	EZ		700,000 est.
BC-50bA				WE		200,000 est.
BC-50bA				WF		400,000 est.
BC-50bA				WL		100,000 est.
BC-50bA				WN		400,000 est.
BC-50bA				WV		400,000 est.
BC-50bA				YA		400,000 est.
BC-50b	$20	1969	Lawson-Bouey; 2 letters	YA-YH		79,750,000

Summary of Technical Details (Cont'd.)

Cat.No.	Denom.	Date	Variety	Prefixes	Numbers	Qty. Printed
BC-51a	$50	1975	Lawson-Bouey; 2 letters	HA-HD		36,456,000
BC-51aA	$50	1975	Asterisk Note	HB		300,000 est.
BC-51aA				HC		100,000 est.
BC-51a-i	$50	1975	Lawson-Bouey; 3 letters	EHA-EHF		56,440,000
BC-51aA-i	$50	1975	Replacement Note	EHX	0000000-9999999	420,000
BC-51b	$50	1975	Crow-Bouey	EHF-EHM		In issue
BC-51bA	$50	1975	Replacement Note	EHX	0420000-	In issue
BC-52a	$100	1975	Lawson-Bouey; 2 letters	JA-JD		35,400,000
BC-52aA	$100	1975	Asterisk Note	JA		200,000 est.
BC-52aA				JC		100,000 est.
BC-52a-i	$100	1975	Lawson-Bouey; 3 letters	AJA-AJC		22,400,000
BC-52aA	$100	1975	Replacement Note	AJX	0000000-0199999	200,000
BC-52b	$100	1975	Crow-Bouey	AJC-AJJ		In issue
BC-52bA	$100	1975	Replacement Note	AJX	0200000-	In issue

$1 Issue — 1973

BC-46a-i

Face Design: Coat of Arms of Canada/—/Queen Elizabeth II
Colour: Green multicoloured tint

BC-46a-i

Back Design: —/Parliament Hill, across the Ottawa River/—
Colour: Green, blue tint

Issue Date: Engraved: 1973   **Imprint:** None

Signatures
Left: Engr. R.W. Lawson   **Right:** Engr. G.K. Bouey
Engr. J.W. Crow   Engr. G.K. Bouey

Official First Day of Issue: June 3, 1974

Cat. No.	Denom.	Date	Variety	VF	EF	AU	Unc
BC-46a	$1	1973	Lawson-Bouey; 2 letters	1.00	1.50	3.00	3.75
BC-46aA	$1	1973	Lawson-Bouey; 2 letters	1.50	2.25	3.50	6.00
BC-46a-i	$1	1973	Lawson-Bouey; 3 letters	1.00	1.50	2.00	3.50
BC-46aA-i	$1	1973	Lawson-Bouey; 3 letters	1.50	2.25	3.50	6.00
BC-46aT-i	$1	1973	Lawson-Bouey; Prefix AXA	40.00	60.00	90.00	150.00
BC-46b	$1	1973	Crow-Bouey; 3 letters	1.00	1.00	1.25	2.00
BC-46bA	$1	1973	Crow-Bouey; 3 letters	1.50	2.25	3.50	6.00
BC-46bT-i	$1	1973	Crow-Bouey; Prefix AXA	40.00	60.00	90.00	150.00

$2 Issue — 1974

BC-47aAi

Face Design: Coat of Arms of Canada/—/Queen Elizabeth II
Colour: Terra Cotta, multicoloured tint

BC-47aAi

Back Design: —/Inuit hunting scene, Baffin Island/—
Colour: Terra Cotta, multicoloured tint

Issue Date: Engraved: 1974   **Imprint:** None
Signatures
Left: Engr. R.W. Lawson   **Right:** Engr. G.K. Bouey
Engr. J.W. Crow   Engr. G.K. Bouey

Official First Day of Issue: August 5, 1975

Cat. No.	Denom.	Date	Variety	VF	EF	AU	Unc
BC-47a	$2	1974	Lawson-Bouey; 2 letters	2.00	2.25	3.00	4.00
BC-47aA	$2	1974	Lawson-Bouey; 2 letters	5.00	7.00	10.00	16.00
BC-47aT	$2	1974	Lawson-Bouey; Prefix RS	125.00	200.00	300.00	475.00
BC-47a-i	$2	1974	Lawson-Bouey; 3 letters	2.00	2.25	3.00	4.00
BC-47aA-i	$2	1974	Lawson-Bouey; 3 letters	25.00	40.00	55.00	90.00
BC-47b	$2	1974	Crow-Bouey; 3 letters	2.00	2.25	3.00	4.00
BC-47bA	$2	1974	Crow-Bouey; 3 letters	30.00	45.00	60.00	100.00

$5 Issue — 1972

BC-48a

Face Design: Coat of Arms of Canada/—/Sir Wilfrid Laurier
Colour: Blue with multicoloured tint

BC-48a

Back Design: —/Salmon seiner, Johnstone Strait, Vancouver Island/—
Colour: Blue with multicoloured tint

Issue Date: Engraved: 1972	**Imprint:** None

Signatures

Left: Engr. G.K. Bouey	**Right:** Engr. L. Rasminsky
Engr. R.W. Lawson	Engr. G.K. Bouey

Official First Day of Issue: December 4, 1972

Cat. No.	Denom.	Date	Variety	VF	EF	AU	Unc
BC-48a	$5	1972	Bouey-Rasminsky; 2 letters	6.	9.	13.	20.
BC-48aA	$5	1972	Bouey-Rasminsky; 2 letters	10.	15.	22.	35.
BC-48b	$5	1972	Lawson-Bouey; 2 letters	6.	9.	13.	20.
BC-48bA	$5	1972	Lawson-Bouey; 2 letters	8.	12.	18.	30.
BC-48bT	$5	1972	Lawson-Bouey; Prefix RS	125.	200.	300.	475.

$10 Issue — 1971

BC-49a

Face Design: Coat of Arms of Canada/—/Sir John A. Macdonald
Colour: Purple with multicoloured tint

BC-49a

Back Design: —/Industrial scene, Sarnia, Ontario/—
Colour: Purple with multicoloured tint

Issue Date: Engraved: 1971	**Imprint:** None

Signatures

Left: Engr. J.R. Beattie	**Right:** Engr. L. Rasminsky
Engr. G.K. Bouey	Engr. L. Rasminsky
Engr. R.W. Lawson	Engr. G.K. Bouey
Engr. G.G. Thiessen	Engr. J.W. Crow

Official First Day of Issue: November 8, 1971

Cat. No.	Denom.	Date	Variety	VF	EF	AU	Unc
BC-49a	$10	1971	Beattie-Rasminsky; 2 letters	15.	23.	35.	50.
BC-49aA	$10	1971	Beattie-Rasminsky; 2 letters	16.	24.	36.	60.
BC-49b	$10	1971	Bouey-Rasminsky; 2 letters	20.	30.	45.	75.
BC-49bA	$10	1971	Bouey-Rasminsky; 2 letters	16.	25.	38.	65.
BC-49c	$10	1971	Lawson-Bouey; 2 letters	10.	12.	15.	25.
BC-49cA	$10	1971	Lawson-Bouey; 2 letters	14.	22.	33.	55.
BC-49c-i	$10	1971	Lawson-Bouey; 3 letters	10.	12.	15.	25.
BC-49cA-i	$10	1971	Lawson-Bouey; 3 letters	14.	22.	33.	55.
BC-49d	$10	1971	Crow-Bouey; 3 letters	10.	12.	15.	25.
BC-49dA	$10	1971	Crow-Bouey; 3 letters	16.	24.	36.	60.
BC-49e	$10	1971	Thiessen-Crow, 3 letters	10.	10.	12.	20.
BC-49eA	$10	1971	Thiessen-Crow, 3 letters	25.	40.	60.	100.

BC-50a

Face Design: Coat of Arms of Canada/—/Queen ELizabeth II
Colour: Olive green with multicoloured tint

BC-50a

Back Design: —/Moraine Lake, Alberta/—
Colour: Olive green with multicoloured tint

Issue Date: Engraved: 1969   **Imprint:** None

Signatures
Left: Engr. J.R. Beattie   **Right:** Engr. L. Rasminsky
Engr. R.W. Lawson   Engr. G.K. Bouey

Official First Day of Issue: June 22, 1970

Cat. No.	Denom.	Date	Variety	VF	EF	AU	Unc
BC-50a	$20	1969	Beattie-Rasminsky; 2 letters	22.	24.	30.	45.
BC-50aA	$20	1969	Beattie-Rasminsky; 2 letters	28.	40.	50.	70.
BC-50b	$20	1969	Lawson-Bouey; 2 letters	21.	23.	25.	40.
BC-50bA	$20	1969	Lawson-Bouey; 2 letters	28.	40.	50.	70.

$50 Issue — 1975

BC-51b

Face Design: Coat of Arms of Canada/—/
William Lyon Mackenzie King
Colour: Red with multicoloured tint

BC-51b

Back Design: —/R.C.M.P. Musical Ride dome formation/—
Colour: Red with multicoloured tint

Issue Date: Engraved: 1975		**Imprint:** None

Signatures

Left: Engr. R.W. Lawson
Engr. J.W. Crow
Engr. G.G. Thiessen

Right: Engr. G.K. Bouey
Engr. G.K. Bouey
Engr. J.W. Crow

Official First Day of Issue: March 31, 1975

Cat. No.	Denom.	Date	Variety	VF	EF	AU	Unc
BC-51a	$50	1975	Lawson-Bouey; 2 letters	50.	55.	65.	75.
BC-51aA	$50	1975	Lawson-Bouey; 2 letters	50.	75.	100.	150.
BC-51a-i	$50	1975	Lawson-Bouey; 3 letters	50.	55.	65.	75.
BC-51aA-i	$50	1975	Lawson-Bouey; 3 letters	55.	70.	95.	125.
BC-51b	$50	1975	Crow-Bouey; 3 letters	50.	50.	55.	60.
BC-51bA	$50	1975	Crow-Bouey; 3 letters	50.	60.	80.	100.
BC-51c	$50	1975	Thiessen-Crow; 3 letters	50.	50.	52.	55.
BC-51cA	$50	1975	Thiessen-Crow; 3 letters	50.	50.	52.	55.

BC-52b

Face Design: Coat of Arms of Canada/—/Sir Robert Borden
Colour: Brown with multicoloured tint

BC-52b

Back Design: —/fishing fleet on the East Coast/—
Colour: Brown with multicoloured tint

Issue Date: Engraved: 1975   **Imprint:** None
Signatures
Left: Engr. R.W. Lawson   **Right:** Engr. G.K. Bouey
Engr. J.W. Crow   Engr. G.K. Bouey
Engr. G.G. Thiessen   Engr. J.W. Crow

Official First Day of Issue: May 31, 1976

Cat. No.	Denom.	Date	Variety	VF	EF	AU	Unc
BC-52a	$100	1975	Lawson-Bouey; 2 letters	100.	105.	115.	130.
BC-52aA	$100	1975	Lawson-Bouey; 2 letters	105.	110.	125.	150.
BC-52a-i	$100	1975	Lawson-Bouey; 3 letters	100.	105.	115.	125.
BC-52aA-i	$100	1975	Lawson-Bouey; 3 letters	105.	110.	125.	150.
BC-52b	$100	1975	Crow-Bouey; 3 letters	100.	105.	115.	125.
BC-52bA	$100	1975	Crow-Bouey; 3 letters	105.	110.	125.	150.
BC-52c	$100	1975	Thiessen-Crow; 3 letters	100.	100.	100.	110.
BC-52cA	$100	1975	Thiessen-Crow; 3 letters	100.	100.	100.	110.

Issues of 1979

The method of numbering the $5 and $20 notes was changed to a format which, it was believed, would be machine readable. The red and blue serial numbers were removed from the note faces, and replaced by black numbers printed on the backs. The BANK OF CANADA BANQUE DU CANADA inscription was removed from below the back vignette to provide a white background for the numbers. The previous $5 and $20 multicolour notes were not withdrawn but permitted to wear out in circulation.

Additional changes were made on the $20 note in response to the criticism that it was not sufficiently different from the $1 note to prevent confusion. The counters in the corners were clarified and strengthened, and the green tones of the face were reduced while the orange and pink tones were enhanced to increase the colour contract between the $20 and the $1.

It was planned to convert the $10, $50 and $100 notes eventually to the black serial number format. That plan was abandoned when it was discovered that the new notes were not machine readable after all.

PREFIXES AND NUMBERING

On the back format the black serial numbers consist of eleven digits, the first of which is characteristic of the denomination. The $5 notes have the denominational number 3 and the $20 notes begin with the denominational number 5. The next number indicates the printer, "0" or "2" denoting CBN and "6" BABN. Only the $20 notes have two printers. The next two digits indicate the series number and the last seven digits provide the number of the note within the series. The note numbers start at 0000000 and end at 9999999, so that each series consists of ten million notes, as in the past.

SIGNATURES

Signatures of the following Bank of Canada officials occur on notes of the 1979 issues. In all cases the signatures are engraved on the face plates.

Senior Deputy Governor	Term of Office
R. William Lawson	March 1, 1973 to Feb. 29, 1984
John W. Crow	March 1, 1984 to Jan. 31, 1987
Gordon G. Thiessen	Oct. 27, 1987 to date

Governor	Term of Office
Gerald K. Bouey	Feb. 1, 1973 to Feb. 1, 1987
John W. Crow	Jan. 31, 1987 to date

IMPRINTS

No imprints are seen on this issue. The second digit of the serial number is used to denote the printer: "0" or "2" for CBN and "6" for BABN. Only the $20 note was supplied by both printers.

REPLACEMENT NOTES

There are no asterisk notes in this issue. The replacement notes are designated by the second digit in the serial number.

The digit 1 following the first digit 3 of the $5 notes designates a replacement note. In the $20 denomination the replacement notes can be distinguished by "510" for the CBN company and "516" for the BABN company.

$5 Replacement note

31003212852 CINQ

BC-53aA

31003340640

BC-53bA

$20 Replacement note

VINGT
51003035676

BC-54aA

VINGT
51003482059

BC-54bA

VINGT
51600017206

BC-54bAi

EXPERIMENTAL NOTES

Only experimental notes in the $5 issue are known. As in the past, they were released to test wearing properties of new papers or inks.

The digit 3 following the first digit 3 (denominational number) of the $5 note's serial number signifies an experimental note. Test or experimental notes are numbered by using "T" in the catalogue number.

$5 Experimental Note

33000059358   33000059358   CINQ

BC-53aT

Summary of Technical Details 1979

Cat.No.	Denom.	Variety	Printer	Series	Numbers	Qty. Printed
BC-53a	$5	Lawson-Bouey	CBN	"30"	30000000000-30461319998	461,319,999
BC-53aA	$5	Replacement Note	CBN	"31"	31000000000-31003319999	3,320,000*
BC-53a	$5	Test Note	CBN	"33"		400,000
BC-53b	$5	Crow-Bouey	CBN	"30"	30461319999-30583019999	121,700,000
BC-53bA	$5	Replacement Note	CBN	"31"	31003320000-31003959997	639,997*
BC-54a	$20	Lawson-Bouey	CBN	"50"	50000000000-50675999999	676,000,000
BC-54aA	$20	Replacement Note	CBN	"510"	51000000000-51003479999	3,480,000
BC-54b	$20	Crow-Bouey	CBN	"50"	50676000000-50999999999	324,000,000
BC-54b	$20	Crow-Bouey	CBN	"52"	52000000000-	In issue
BC-54bA	$20	Replacement Note	CBN	"510"	51003480000-	In issue
BC-54b	$20	Crow-Bouey	BABN	"56"	56000000000-	In issue
BC-54bA-i	$20	Replacement Note	BABN	"516"	51600000000-	In issue
BC-54c	$20	Thiessen-Crow	CBN	"52"		In issue
BC-54cA	$20	Replacement Note	CBN	"510"		In issue
BC-54c-i	$20	Thiessen-Crow	BABN			Not in issue at presstime
BC-54cA-i	$20	Replacement Note	BABN			Not in issue at presstime

Note: 998,999 $5 "31" replacement notes were damaged and destroyed.

$5 Issue — 1979

BC-53a

Face Design: Coat of Arms of Canada/—/Sir Wilfrid Laurier
Colour: Blue with multicoloured tint

BC-53aA

Back Design: —/Salmon fishing off the West Coast/—
Colour: Blue with multicoloured tint

Issue Date: Engraved: 1979   **Imprint:** None
Signatures
Left: Engr. R.W. Lawson   **Right:** Engr. G.K. Bouey
Engr. J.W. Crow   Engr. G.K. Bouey

Official First Day of Issue: October 1, 1979

Cat. No.	Denom.	Date	Variety	VF	EF	AU	Unc
BC-53a	$5	1979	Lawson-Bouey	5.	7.	10.	15.
BC-53aA	$5	1979	Lawson-Bouey	55.	70.	90.	125.
BC-53aT	$5	1979	Lawson-Bouey "33"	350.	435.	550.	900.
BC-53b	$5	1979	Crow-Bouey	5.	7.	10.	15.
BC-53bA	$5	1979	Crow-Bouey	100.	150.	225.	375.

$20 Issue — 1979

BC-54b-i

Face Design: Coat of Arms of Canada/—/Queen Elizabeth II
Colour: Orange and pink with multicoloured tint

BC-54b-i

Back Design: —/lake and Rocky Mountains/—
Colour: Orange and pink with multicoloured tint

Issue Date: Engraved: 1979   **Imprint:** None
Signatures
Left: Engr. R.W. Lawson   **Right:** Engr. G.K. Bouey
Engr. J.W. Crow   Engr. G.K. Bouey
Engr. G.G. Thiessen   Engr. J.W. Crow

Official First Day of Issue: December 18, 1978

Cat. No.	Denom.	Date	Variety	Printer	VF	EF	AU	Unc
BC-54a	$20	1979	Lawson-Bouey	CBN	20.	25.	35.	60.
BC-54aA	$20	1979	Lawson-Bouey	CBN	20.	30.	45.	75.
BC-54b	$20	1979	Crow-Bouey	CBN	20.	22.	25.	35.
BC-54bA	$20	1979	Crow-Bouey	CBN	20.	25.	35.	60.
BC-54b-i	$20	1979	Crow-Bouey	BABN	20.	22.	25.	35.
BC-54bA-i	$20	1979	Crow-Bouey	BABN	20.	25.	35.	60.
BC-54c	$20	1979	Thiessen-Crow	CBN	20.	22.	25.	35.
BC-54cA	$20	1979	Thiessen-Crow	CBN	20.	25.	55.	60.

Issues of 1986 — To Date

On March 14, 1986, the Bank of Canada introduced a new series of banknotes. The new designs were launched that year with the issue of the $2 and $5 notes. The Bank of Canada has not undertaken a redesign of the $1 note because of the Government of Canada's decision to introduce a new one-dollar coin for wide circulation in Canada during 1987. The $1 note will not be distributed after June of 1989.

This series of notes incorporates new security features against counterfeiting as well as changes which will facilitate more efficient use of high-speed note sorting machines. In addition the series incorporates features to assist the blind and visually impaired to distinguish among denominations of notes.

A number of characteristics of the new banknotes are the same as those on the 1969-1975 issues. The notes are the same size and printed on the same paper. The dominant colour of each denomination remains unchanged. The portrait subjects on the front of each denomination are the same as in the 1969-1975 issues but the portraits are larger. A new portrait of Her Majesty Queen Elizabeth II was engraved. It first appears on the new $2 note and subsequently on the $20 and $1000 notes. New portraits of the four Prime Ministers who appear on the notes of the 1969-1975 issues — Sir John A. Macdonald, Sir Wilfrid Laurier, Sir Robert Borden and William Lyon Mackenzie King — have been engraved for the $10, $5, $100 and $50 denominations, respectively. The names of the Prime Ministers appear beside their portraits.

The designs on the back of each denomination of the new series are completely different. They feature birds found across Canada as the main focal point in a landscape and a stylized background sky depicting the word "Canada". The $2 note will portray the Robin; the $5 note, the Belted Kingfisher, the $10 note, the Osprey; the $20 note, the Common Loon, the $50 note, the Snowy Owl; and the $100 note, the Canada Goose. In the case of the $1000 note a decision has not yet been made. Each bird is identified by name.

For several years the Bank of Canada has been assessing methods of making denominations of banknotes distinguishable by the blind and the visually impaired. To assist the blind, the notes of this series are printed so that the denomination can be read by a small hand-held electronic device now under development in consultation with the national offices of the Canadian National Institute for the Blind and the Canadian Council of the Blind. The electronic devise will "speak" the denomination in either English or French. The new series has larger and more distinct counters which will also help the visually impaired.

PREFIXES AND NUMBERING

The triple letter prefix, first introduced in 1981, forms part of the serial number for this issue. The first letter designates the printer, the second letter denotes the denomination, and the third indicates the series. The series letters may include all letters from "A to Z" excepting I, O, Q and X, the first three due to their resemblance to numerals and the last for its use to denote a replacement note. Each series is numbered from 0000000 to 9999999, with the zero note being removed and destroyed prior to issue. Thus any given denominational letter may accommodate twenty-two series, or 220,000,000 notes.

The series is back-numbered right and left in black similar to the 1979 issues. However, besides the triple prefix difference each denomination carries a barcode to the left of the serial number which can be read by banknote sorting and counting equipment.

SIGNATURES

Signatures of the following Bank of Canada officials occur on notes of the 1986 issues. In all cases the signatures are engraved on the face plates.

The changeover from Crow-Bouey to the Thiessen-Crow signature combination on the 1986 issue $2 notes was unusually protracted. Previously, normal practise had been to terminate one signature combination at a precise point in the numbering of a particular series and begin the new signature combination immediately after that point. In the case of the $2 1986, both signature combinations appear on various notes of series AUG, AUH, AUJ, AUK, AUL, AUM, AUN and ARX, well mixed in terms of numbers.

It is understood that two presses were ar work on $2 note production simultaneoulsy, one equipped with plates bearing the engraved Crow-Bouey signatures and the other having plates engraved Thiessen-Crow. However, only one machine was used in applying the serial numbers to the otherwise finished notes. No effort was made to keep separate the notes produced from the two presses during numbering, so they were numbered sequentially from more or less randomly selected piles.

Senior Deputy Governor	*Term of Office*
John W. Crow	March 1, 1984 to February 1, 1987
Gordon G. Thieseen	October 27, 1987 to date

Governor	*Term of Office*
Gerald K. Bouey	February 1, 1973 to February 1, 1987
John W. Crow	February 1, 1987 To Date

IMPRINTS

There are no imprints on these notes. The British American and Canadian Bank Note Companies have participated in the printing.

The first letter of the triple prefix letters indicate the printer: "A" for BABN and "B" for CBN. The $2 notes are currently printed by BABN with the CBN printing the $5 note.

PLATE NUMBERS

A yellow plate number was used on the backs of the $5 notes for the series ENA-ENZ and EOA-EOH. The plate number was then changed to blue. A similar change took place in the replacement (ENX) notes.

REPLACEMENT NOTES

As in the triple prefix notes of the 1969-1975 issues, the identification of replacement notes is continued by the use of an "X" for the third letter.

$2 Replacement Note	**$5 Replacement Note**
BC-55aA	**BC-56aA**

EXPERIMENTAL NOTES

No experimental notes are known to exist at publication date.

Checklist of Prefix Letters for 1986 Issues

Cat.No.	Denom.	Date	Variety	Denom. Letter	Series Letter
BC-55a	$2	1986	Crow-Bouey	AR	F G H J K L M N P R T U V W Y Z
BC-55a	$2	1986	Crow-Bouey	AU	A B C D E F G H J K L M N
BC-55aA	$2	1986	Crow-Bouey	AR	X
BC-55b	$2	1986	Thiessen-Crow	AU	G H J K L M N P R S T U V W Y Z
BC-55b	$2	1986	Thiessen-Crow	BA	A
BC-55bA	$2	1986	Thiessen-Crow	AR	X
BC-56a	$5	1986	Crow-Bouey	EN	A B C D E F G H J K L M N P R S T U V W Y Z
BC-56a	$5	1986	Crow-Bouey	EP	A B
BC-56a	$5	1986	Crow-Bouey	EO	A B C D E F G H J K L M N P R S T U V W Y Z
BC-56aA	$5	1986	Crow-Bouey	EN	X

Summary of Technical Details

Cat.No.	Denom.	Date	Variety	Prefixes	Numbers	Qty. Printed
BC-55a	$2	1986	Crow-Bouey	ARF-ARZ	0000000-9999999	16,000,000
BC-55a	$2	1986	Crow-Bouey	AUA-AUN		Unknown
BC-55aA	$2	1986	Crow-Bouey	ARX		Unknown
BC-55b	$2	1986	Thiessen-Crow	AUG-AUZ		In issue
BC-55b	$2	1986	Thiessen-Crow	BAA		In issue
BC-55bA	$2	1986	Thiessen-Crow	ARX		In issue
BC-56a	$5	1986	Crow-Bouey (yellow back plate #)	ENA-ENZ	0000000-9999999	22,000,000
BC-56a	$5	1986	Crow-Bouey (yellow back plate #)	EOA-EOH		Unknown
BC-56a-i	$5	1986	Crow-Bouey (blue back plate #)	EOH-EOZ		
BC-56a	$5	1986	Crow-Bouey (blue back plate #)	EPA-EPB		In issue
BC-56aA	$5	1986	Crow-Bouey (yellow back plate #)	ENX		In issue
BC-56aA-i	$5	1986	Crow-Bouey (blue back plate #)	ENX		In issue

$2 Issue — 1986

BC-55

Face Design: —/Queen Elizabeth II/Parliament Buildings
Colour: Dark Terra Cotta, Rainbow tint

BC-55

Back Design: —/Robins/—
Colour: Dark Terra Cotta, Rainbow tint

Issue Date: Engraved: 1986

Imprint: None

Printer: British American Bank Note Company

Signatures

Left: Engr. J.W. Crow
Engr. G.G. Thiessen

Right: Engr. G.K. Bouey
Engr. J.W. Crow

Official First Day of Issue: September 2, 1986

Cat. No.	Denom.	Date	Variety	AU	Unc
BC-55a	$2	1986	Crow-Bouey	2.25	3.50
BC-55aA	$2	1986	Crow-Bouey	7.00	10.00
BC-55b	$2	1986	Thiessen-Crow	2.00	3.00
BC-55bA	$2	1986	Thiessen-Crow	2.00	4.00

$5 Issue — 1986

BC-56

Face Design: —/Sir Wilfrid Laurier/Parliament Buildings
Colour: Dark blue, Rainbow tint

BC-56

Back Design: —/Belted Kingfisher/—
Colour: Dark blue, Rainbow tint

Issue Date: Engraved: 1986

Imprint: None

Printer: Canadian Bank Note Company

Signatures

Left: Engr. J.W. Crow
Engr. G.G. Thiessen

Right: Engr. G.K. Bouey
Engr. J.W. Crow

Official First Day of Issue: April 28, 1986

Cat. No.	Denom.	Date	Variety	AU	Unc
BC-56a	$5	1986	Crow-Bouey	5.	7.
BC-56aA	$5	1986	Crow-Bouey	5.	8.
BC-56b	$5	1986	Thiessen-Crow	5.	6.
BC-56bA	$5	1986	Thiessen-Crow	5.	7.

$10 Issue of — 1989

**PHOTO UNAVAILABLE
AT PRESSTIME**

BC-57

Face Design: —/Sir John A. Macdonald/Parliament Buildings
with red ensign flag
Colour: Purple, Rainbow tint

Back Design: —/Osprey in flight/—
Colour: Purple, Rainbow tint

Issue Date: Engraved 1989

Imprint: None

Printer: Canadian Bank Note
Company

Signatures
Left: Engr. G.G. Thiessen

Right: Engr. J.W. Crow

Official First Day of Issue: June 1989

Cat. No.	Denom.	Date	Variety	Unc
BC-57a	$10	1989	Thiessen-Crow	12.
BC-57aA	$10	1989	Thiessen-Crow	15.

$20, $50 and $100 Issues
Pre-release information

BC-58 $20 Issue of —

Face Design: Queen Elizabeth II
Colour: Olive green, Rainbow tint
Back Design: Common Loon
Colour: Olive green, Rainbow tint

BC-59 $50 Issue of —

Face Design: William Lyon Mackenzie King
Colour: Red, Rainbow tint
Back Design: Snowy Owl
Colour: Red, Rainbow tint

BC-60 $100 Issue of —

Face Design: Sir Robert Borden
Colour: Brown, Rainbow tint
Back Design: Canada Goose
Colour: Brown, Rainbow tint

BC-61 $1000 Issue of —

Face Design: Queen Elizabeth II
Colour: Rose, Rainbow tint
Back Design: Unknown
Colour: Unknown

SPECIAL SERIAL NUMBERS

Serial numbers are the control numbers for the production, distribution and circulation of notes. They are printed on the notes in what may be termed the overprint stage by electromechanical counters which automatically cycle to the next number as each sheet enters the press.

In the Dominion of Canada and early Bank of Canada series the cycle was one. In the 1954 series the cycle was 500 and currently it is 1000.

Special serial numbers are grouped into six different categories: (1) Palindrome (radar) Notes, (2) Million Numbered Notes, (3) Ascending/Descending "Ladder" Numbered Notes, (4) Low Serial Numbered Notes, (5) Matching Numbered Notes, (6)Changeover serial numbers.

Further subdivisions will occur within these main groups.

Values for Special Serial Numbered notes are formulated on uncirculated condition as this is the grade in which these notes are usually collected. It is naturally understood that some of the rarer combinations of numbers, if found on a lower grade, will have a substantial premium. To construct value tables that incorporate grades at this time is premature. The number of collectors in this specialized field is small but growing and it is hoped that this section will provide helpful information and possibly in future editions the value tables will expand as the market dictates. To obtain a grade value for individual notes in this section the following rule of thumb can be applied.

Almost Unc (AU) value equals 80% of the uncirculated premium.
Extremely Fine (EF) value equals 60% of the uncirculated premium.
Very Fine (VF) value equals 40% of the uncirculated premium.
Fine (F) value equals 25% of the uncirculated premium.
Very Good (VG) value equals 15% of the uncirculated premium.

Please remember that this method will only yield market indications of value with unforeseen supply and demand shifts, altering the percentages dramatically either way.

PALINDROME OR "RADAR" NOTES

A Palindrome or Radar Note, as they are more commonly known, bears a serial number which will read the same from left to right as right to left. Palindrome means a word, verse or sentence which reads the same backward or forward and this meaning was transferred by paper money collectors to the numerals used in serial numbers. A radar is a radio detecting and ranging device. A transmitter sends out microwaves, a receiver detects the echo. If there was no interference then the echo received would simulate the beam sent out. Similarly when a number reading to the right and then "echoing" or reading back from right to left is the same, it would in fact mimic the meaning of the word radar or palindrome. The word "radar" incidentally also reads the same left to right as right to left, thus doubly describing the type of serial number carried by the note. In the 1969-1975 issues of the Bank of Canada when ten million consecutive notes are produced for a specific prefix, a maximum of ten thousand notes may be radar. The number of notes in a radar collection having one note for each prefix combination is the same as needed for a prefix collection, over three hundred for all the prefixes of the one dollar issue of 1973. However a radar collection would be much more difficult to assemble.

SOLID NUMBERED "RADAR" NOTES

A special type of radar note is the "Solid" Numbered Note where the serial number is made up of one digit, for example; the numbers 1111111, 2222222, etc. These are called "solid" numbers. For every ten million consecutive notes produced, a maximum of nine notes may have a "solid" number. These are the most desirable variety of "radar" notes.

Issue	Type	Price Range
1954	Devil's Face	Catalogue value plus $125.-$200.
1954	Modified	Catalogue value plus $50.-$75.
1967	$1 Confederation	Catalogue value plus $100.-$150.
1969-1975	Multicoloured Issues	Catalogue value plus $75.-$125.
1979-1989	11 digit numbers	Extremely Rare

TWO DIGIT NUMBERED "RADAR" NOTES

A Two Digit "Radar" Numbered Note is one where the serial number is made up of only two digits repeated throughout the serial number, for example; the numbers 1001001, 4244424 and 5552555 are two digit numbered notes.

Issue	Type	Price Range
1954	Devil's Face	Catalogue value plus $50.-$100.
1954	Modified	Catalogue value plus $25.-$50.
1967 $1	Confederation	Catalogue value plus $50.-$100.
1969-1975	Multicoloured Issues	Catalogue value plus $20.-$35.
1979-1989	11 digit numbers	Very Rare

THREE AND FOUR DIGIT "RADAR" NOTES

Three and four digit "radar" notes are notes in which the sheet number is comprised of 3 or 4 digits. These are the most commonly found "radar" notes.

3 Digit	4 Digit
1377731	1459541
4421244	6580856
2124212	0914190

Issue	Price Range
Issues before 1967	Catalogue value plus $20.-$35.
1967 Issues	Catalogue value plus $25.-$50.
Multicolour Issues	Catalogue value plus $5.-$10.

ASCENDING/DESCENDING "LADDER" "RADAR" NUMBERED NOTES

Consecutive ascending and descending numbers will combine to form radar combinations which are almost in the same class of rarity as solid numbers.

In a ten million consecutive sequence of notes, a maximum of sixteen notes may be called consecutive Ascending/Descending or Descending/Ascending "Radar" Numbered Notes.

Ascending/Descending "Radar" Combinations		Descending/Ascending "Radar" Combinations	
0123210	1234321	0987890	9876789
2345432	3456543	8765678	7654567
4567654	5678765	6543456	5432345
6789876	7890987	4321234	3210123

Issue	Type	Price Range
1954	Devil's Face	Catalogue value plus $50.-$100.
1954	Modified	Catalogue value plus $25.-$50
1967 $1	Confederation	Catalogue value plus $50.-$100.
1969-1975	Multicoloured Issues	Catalogue value plus $25.-$50.
1979-1989	11 digit numbers	Very Rare

CONSECUTIVE ASCENDING OR DESCENDING
"LADDER" NUMBERED NOTES

Ascending or Descending serial numbered notes are illustrated below. In a ten million consecutive sequence of notes, a maximum of ten notes will be found with consecutive ascending or descending serial numbers. these are the most desirable, but non-consecutive numbers are also collected.

Ascending		Descending	
0123456	1234567	6543210	7654321
2345678	3456789	8765432	9876543
4567890		0987654	

Issue	Type	Price Range
1954	Devil's Face	Catalogue value plus $50.-$100.
1954	Modified	Catalogue value plus $25.-$50.
1967	$1 Confederation	Catalogue value plus $50.-$100.
1969-1975	Multicoloured	Catalogue value plus $25.-$50.
1979-1989	11 digit numbers	Very Rare

MILLION NUMBERED NOTES

A Million Serial Number Note is one in which the serial number is all zeros preceded by any number from 1 to 10.

Before 1968, ten million numbered notes were printed by the Bank of Canada for the issues of 1935, 1937, 1954 and 1967. With these notes the last zero was printed on by hand as the numbering device could only print to 9999999

In the new issues with 11 digits (1979-1989), the first digit designating the denomination (3 for $5 notes, 5 for $20 notes) would not be included, such that a number like 30090000000 would be a ninety million numbered note.

Few collectors before 1954 are known to have collected this type of special sheet numbers and they are very scarce. Their values would vary widely if they were offered for sale and so will not be priced at this time.

The approximate number of notes issued with a ten million serial number is shown in the following table.

Issue	Denomination							
	$1	$2	$5	$10	$20	$50	$100	$1000
1935	4	0	0	0	0	0	0	0
1937	78	28	24	28	7	0	0	0
1954	125	53	49	39	21	1	1	0
1967	13	0	0	0	0	0	0	0

Source: Canadian Prefix Newsletter

Using the occurrence numbers of the above table and multiplying these by nine will approximate the number of million numbered notes produced for the same issues.

Million numbered notes are found at the bottom of a bundle of notes and since these bundles were wrapped with a paper band around them, many will be found in EF to AU condition because of some minor edge wrinkles or folds.

Million Serial Number Values

Issue	Type	Price Range
1954	Devil's Face	Catalogue value plus $150.-$200.
1954	Modified	Catalogue value plus $25.-$75.
1967	$1 Confederation	Catalogue value plus $75.-$125.
1969-1975	Multicoloured	Catalogue value plus $50.-$75.
1979-1989	11 digit numbers	Very Rare

Ten Million Serial Number Values

Issue	Type	Price Range
1954	Devil's Face	Very Rare
1954	Modified	Catalogue value plus $300.-$500.
1967	$1 Confederation	Very Rare
1969-1975	Multicoloured	Very Rare
1979-1989	11 digit numbers	Very Rare

LOW SERIAL NUMBERED NOTES

A bank note with a sheet number less 25 may be classified as a Low Serial Numbered Note. Notes with matching numbers for different denominations were sometimes given as presentation sets. Notes in this category are generally AU to Uncirculated.

Generally a bank note with a sheet number of less than 500 could be considered to have a low serial number. Sheet numbers of less than 25 or in some cases less than 100 would be in higher demand, as would numbers less than 10. Some collectors try to obtain matching low numbers from different types and denominations of notes. Thus the scarcer the type and the lower the number, the higher the premium paid for the note. Notes with sheet number 1 are eagerly sought after by some collectors. Most of these notes are in AU to UNC condition The value of these notes depends on the Issue , the particular number and its condition and these would vary widely. Only a rough price range will be attempted.

Issue	Type	Price Range
1954	Devil's Face	Catalogue value plus $25.-$200.
1954	Modified	Catalogue value plus $10.-$125.
1967	$1 Confederation	Catalogue value plus $25.-$200.
1969-1975	Multicoloured	Catalogue value plus $10.-$75.
1979-1989	11 digit numbers	Very Scarce

MATCHING SHEET NUMBERED SETS

This category consists of a set of notes of different denominations, usually of the same issue, having the same sheet number. As with the Low Serial Numbered Notes, Matched Sets are usually low numbers collected at the Bank of Canada for presentation and for the multi-coloured issues obtained from the Bank of Canada for the Canadian Paper Money Society members. It is all but impossible to obtain a set of notes in denomination order that will have matching serial numbers from circulated notes.

Issue	No. of Notes	Denom.	Set Value
1954 Devil's Face	8	$1 to $1000	Catalogue value plus 100%
	7	$1 to $100	Catalogue value plus 100%
	6	$1 to $50	Catalogue value plus 100%
	5	$1 to $20	Catalogue value plus 100%
	4	$1 to $10	Catalogue value plus 100%
1954 Modified	8	$1 to $1000	Catalogue value plus 25%-50%
	7	$1 to $100	Catalogue value plus 25%-50%
	6	$1 to $50	Catalogue value plus 25%-50%
	5	$1 to $20	Catalogue value plus 25%-50%
	4	$1 to $10	Catalogue value plus 25%-50%
1969-1975 2 letters	7	$1 to $100	Catalogue value plus 10%-25%
or 3 letter prefix	6	$1 to $50	Catalogue value plus 10%-25%
	5	$1 to $20	Catalogue value plus 10%-25%
	4	$1 to $10	Catalogue value plus 10%-25%

CHANGEOVER NUMBERED NOTES

Changeover numbers are the numbers that occur at the end of one signature combination and at the beginning of the next signature combination when the same prefix letter combination is continued from the first type to the second type: Eg. BC-29a 7,200,000 to BC-29b 7,200,001. Although none of these exact numbers are known in private collections (most are in the Bank of Canada National Collection) the numbers coming as close as possible to these numbers are sought after by a few collectors. They are usually in circulated condition. the premium value for these numbers has not been determined as they have not been offered publicly.

Similarly high and low numbers of many of the asterisk or replacement notes are collected by a few as in most cases the actual number printed is at present unknown to collectors.

PAPER MONEY ERRORS

Paper money errors of Chartered and Private Bank Notes, Province and Dominion of Canada notes, and the 1935 and 1937 Bank of Canada notes are seldom encountered. The smaller quantities produced and the slower printing processes meant less chance of errors being produced and then escaping undetected. Also with fewer error note collectors those errors of the large-size notes that did reach circulation were more likely not saved.

The following listings of major categories of bank note errors have been produced to allow the collector to quickly and easily determine the value of most paper money errors based upon their appearance. The more unusual, startling or dramatic the appearance of the error the higher the value placed on it by collectors.

The production sequence for current Canadian paper money is back tint, face tint, face intaglio printing, overprinting and cutting. From 1935 to 1986 a sheet carried thirty-two note impressions, after 1968 the sheet size was increased to give 40 note impressions.

The 1935, 1937, 1954 Devil's Face and a large segment of 1954 Modified issues were produced 32 on. From 1935 to 1968 the serial numbers and signatures were added by the Bank of Canada in a final pass through a press, the overprinting stage. After 1968 only the serial numbers were added during the overprinting by the Bank of Canada. The signatures were now engraved on the face plates and printed during the face printing process at the Bank Note Company.

Valuations for error notes are listed with a price range covering EF to Unc condition. To the values listed must be added the face value of the note if over $5. As a general rule paper money errors are most avidly collected in the lower denominations, but a few collectors are willing to pay for errors in higher denomination notes. Contrary to expectation, a high denomination note or a rare note will often draw less premium as an error. Error notes are generally collected and found in uncirculated condition. Remember this is the area of the specialist and most will already have an example of a common error in their collection.

Replacement notes, (which have replaced errors found during the quality control process of the printers or at the Bank of Canada,) with errors will often carry a higher premium value.

Some error notes, especially the more spectacular or multiple varieties, cannot be evaluated in a catalogue. Their value must be determined on an individual basis between buyer and seller.

These spectacular or multiple error notes very rarely find their way through the inspection process. With multiple errors the simple procedure of adding each individual type of error value together to obtain an overall value is insufficient. The multiple error note will move quickly into its own special category and its value must be determined on an individual basis. Likewise the value of large and spectacular errors will also be individually determined.

Some types of errors naturally lend themselves to fakery. The addition or removal of ink to simulate a genuine printing error can be accomplished. Colour changes from green to blue, brown or yellow can easily be produced by the application of bleach or alkali to a note. Asterisks and sheet numbers can also be removed. Cutting errors can now be created from the $1 uncut sheets being sold by the Bank of Canada. Collectors should view notes from the newly released uncut sheets with suspicion if they surface as cutting errors.

FACE OR BACK PRINTING ERRORS

Incomplete Printing

Any note which has had all or a portion of the face or back design left unprinted. An example is a note showing only the face or back design leaving the other completely missing, usually as a result of two sheets being fed through the press at the same time. In the case of the face design missing, the only printing might be the overprinted serial numbers and signatures on the notes prior to 1968. Incomplete printing can also result from insufficient ink. When a note displays weak, missing or irregular printing of the face or back design it may be caused by defects in the inking system or problems with the ink, or with other parts of the press which are used to apply ink to the plate.

Printing Error	Price Range
Missing face or back printing up to 25%	$50.-$150.
Missing face or back printing over 25%	$100.-$300.
Missing face or back printing 100%	$200.-$500.

Ink Smears

Occasionally a note may be found with various amounts of the printing ink in streaks or irregular patches on the face or back of the note. This is probably caused by incomplete wiping of the plate between rotations. They have been seen mostly on 1954 note issues.

Printing Error	Price Range
Ink Smears	$25.-$100.

Offset Printing

The ink impression of all or part of the design, face or back, is transferred during printing to the face or back of a note resulting in a mirror image being offset to the opposite side of the note. An example of this process is the back design of the note being transferred to the face of the note. The value of offset printing errors depends on the percentage of the design transferred and the clearer (darker the offset image) the transfer.

The second type of offset error is that which is not caused by a transfer of ink from the press directly onto the note, but rather from an excess of ink, or insufficient drying of a sheet, such that the sheet below, after printing, receives an impression from the sheet above or vice versa. This error type is most often seen when the signature appears reversed in the normal position on the back of a note.

10 to 15% Offset

40% Offset

80% Offset

Offset Signatures

Printing Error	Price Range
Offset, face or back, up to 25%	$100.-$200.
Offset, face or back, 25%-75%	$150.-$350.
Offset, face or back, 75%-100%	$200.-$500.
Offset signatures on the back	$50.-$125.

Double Printing

When a sheet is fed through the printing press twice. This error will show two complete images of the face or back design. Very rare.

Double Denomination Notes

This error would be caused by a sheet of one denomination printed on one side being turned over and passed through a press printing a different denomination. This type of error has not been confirmed for a Canadian note.

Out of Register Printing

A note that has the face or back printed out of the normal centered position due to faulty feeding of sheets through the press or by misalignment of the plates in the press. Usually either the face or the back of the note will be properly centered. The value of these will depend on the degree of misalignment and usually a misalignment of the face of a note is of more interest than on the back of the note. The larger the amount of the adjoining note printed, the higher the value.

Face Tint 5% Shift to Left

Printing Error	Price Range
Double printing	Very Rare
Double denomination	Not Known
Out of register,	$25.-$100.
Out of register, with adjoining note	$50.-$150.

SIGNATURE ERRORS

Signature errors will appear only on the 1967 and earlier issues. After the Confederation issue signatures were engraved onto the face plate thus being printed at the same time as the engraved face plate. For issues before 1967 the signatures were added (overprinted) by the Bank of Canada.

Misplaced Signatures

Misalignment of the sheet of notes being fed into the press results in signatures overprinted out of position.

Printing Error	Price Range
Normal position signatures printed on back	$100.-$200.
Signatures misaligned on face; up, down or sideways	$75.-$200.
Signatures misaligned on back; up, down or sideways	$75.-$200.

Inverted Signatures

The signatures are printed on the face or back of the note upside down. The sheet was fed into the overprinting press rotated 180 degrees from normal and in some cases also upside down to give an inverted back signature. These are also often out of alignment.

Printing Error	Price Range
Inverted signatures on the face	$125.-$250.
Inverted signatures on the back	$125.-$250.

No Signatures

Notes have completely missed the signature overprinting process.

Printing Error	Price Range
Signatures missing	$100.-$200.

SERIAL NUMBER ERRORS

Serial numbers on all Bank of Canada notes are overprinted by the Bank of Canada in their head office in Ottawa.

Mismatched Prefix Letters

This type of error is rarely found, but would result if the prefix lettering wheels became loose and rotated out of sequence to that printing the opposite side of the note. Usually the sheet number is also mismatched.

Mismatched Sheet Numbers

A note which carries two different sheet numbers. Usually one digit is different, but occasionally 2 or more digits are different.

Printing Error	Price Range
Mismatched, one digit	$25.-$75.
Mismatched, two digits	$50.-$150.
Mismatched, three or more digits	$75.-$200.
Mismatched, prefix letters	Very Rare
Mismatched, digits and prefix	Very Rare

Partial Digit Sheet Number

A note which has one or more digits of the serial number split between two numbers. The numbering device did not rotate completely to the next number or became stuck partly rotated.

Printing Error	Price Range
Partial digit showing, one	$25.-$75.
Partial digit showing, two	$50.-$150.
Partial digit showing, three or more	$75.-$250.

Missing Sheet Number

A note may have all (including the prefix letters) or one or more of the digits missing . Serial numbers can be removed and the collectors should be very cautious when assessing a note with this error.

Missing Sheet Number, Three Digits

Missing Sheet Number, Both Sides

Printing Error	Price Range
Missing numbers, one digit	$25.-$75.
Missing numbers, two or more	$50.-$200.
Missing sheet number, one side	$75.-$150.
Missing sheet number, both sides	$100.-$250.

Misplaced Serial Number

The serial number may be overprinted out of register, inverted (printed upside down in the signature position), overprinted on the back or inverted on the back.

Printing Error	Price Range
Number out of register, up, down, sideways	$50.-$150.
Number inverted on the face	$100.-$250.
Number on the back	$75.-$200.
Number inverted on the back	$100.-$250.

Duplicate Sheet Number

This type of error is very scarce and is caused by one or more digits, starting at the right of the sheet number, in the numbering wheel becoming stuck and thus not rotating to the next number. This results in two or more notes having the same serial number. This type of error is seldom found, partly because it is not evident unless two or more notes are found together.

FOLDING AND CUTTING ERRORS

Folding and cutting errors will generally be found in "Uncirculated" condition.

Single Folds

The paper sheet is either folded or creased before or during printing in such a manner that the resulting single note will show a white streak on the back or a white or partially white streak on the face of the note. Since the face of the note goes through the press twice, either the lithographed tint or the Intaglio printed design, or both may be missing in the folded area. Single vertical folds are commoner than multiple or horizontal folds.

Folding Error	Price Range
Single Fold, One	$25.-$75.
Single Fold, Two or more	$50.-$125.

Multiple Folds

The paper sheet is folded either before of after printing in such a manner that when the sheet is cut, an extra piece of the adjoining note or notes is attached. The attached piece or pieces may be blank or have printing from the face or back of the adjacent notes, depending on when the folding occurred. Folds occurring along the outside of the sheet will sometimes have alignment marks or colour bars appearing on the attached piece. Some double folds will result in three or more pieces of several notes being found together.

Folding Error	Price Range
Multiple Fold, Small part attached	$25.- $75.
Multiple Fold, Large part attached	$75.-$200.
Multiple Fold, more than two notes	$150.-$350.

Inverted Design

The face printing of the note is inverted or upside down in relation to the back printing. Could be caused by the sheet being flipped over and rotated after one side had been printed. It has only been confirmed as an error on a Dominion of Canada 25c 1870 B fractional.

Printing Error	Price Range
Inverted design	Very Rare

Cut Out of Register

A note cut with improper alignment of the sheet in the cutting press or the sheet being folded before cutting. The greater the misalignment the higher the value. Usually part of another note must show to result in a premium value. Sometimes the adjoining paper will show the "colour bar" either at the top or bottom of the note. The more "colour bar" showing the greater the value.

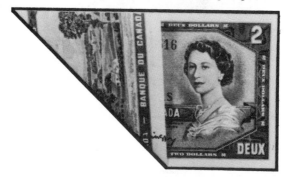

Cut Off Size

Malfunctions in the cutting operation resulting in off size notes. Off size note errors will only apply to notes cut over the standard size, since any note could be made smaller after being issued.

Cutting Error	Price Range
Out of Register, up to 25%	$50.-$100.
Out of Register, 25% or more	$100.-$200.
Out of Register, with colour bar	$200.-$350.

REPLACEMENT NOTE ERRORS

Occasionally the same types of errors found on regularly issued notes can be found on replacement or asterisk notes. However, these will be mostly in the cutting or folding type of errors as most of the printing errors would be discovered when transferring a replacement sheet from its stack to the regular stack of notes. As a general rule, the value of these replacement errors would be 25% to 50% above the value of the same error on a regular issue note.

Printed in Canada